MH370

MYSTERY SOLVED

Web: HVSaviation.com
Contact: contact@HVSaviation.com

Paperback edition
ISBN 978-1-7752834-2-3

Typesetting and Cover Design by FormattingExperts.com

Source for all photographs and illustrations used in this book is provided in the log of figures on pages 130-131. Photographs used in figures 11, 12, 14, 15 and 19-25 and bottom photograph in figure 26, as attributed to ATSB in the log of figures, are sourced from ATSB website at *atsb.gov.au/mh370-pages/resources/images*. These ATSB photographs are licensed under Creative Commons Attribution 4.0 Australia. You can find the original caption for each photograph on ATSB website. ATSB photographs used for figure 26 (except photograph on the bottom) and for figure 9 illustration are licensed under Creative Commons Attribution 3.0 Australia. Figure 16 images: top left image extracted from the photograph by Bill Abbot, licensed under CC BY-SA 2.0; the top right, bottom left and bottom right photographs source and license per figure 11, 14 and 26 attributions respectively. All third-party photographs used in the book were annotated and converted to grayscale for use in this book.

Visit HVSaviation.com/book for links to sources and licenses of CC-licensed photographs, to examine full-color photographs in detail, see different views of wreckage pieces and follow links to sources of technical information and official investigation documents referenced in this book.

MH370
MYSTERY SOLVED

LARRY VANCE

To all the professional aircraft accident investigators
I have had the pleasure to work with over these many years

PREFACE

The aviation accident investigation expertise that made this book possible comes from the combined experience of three individuals who work together as independent consultants, based in Ottawa, Canada. None of us has any connection to the official Malaysia Airlines Flight 370 (MH370) investigation; nor do we have any business connection to the case. Our only objective is to provide our investigation expertise so that the truth about what happened to MH370 can be known.

All three of us had previous careers with what is now called the *Transportation Safety Board of Canada* (TSB), Canada's official government agency responsible for aircraft accident investigation. We now provide independent accident investigation services to clients around the world.

Terry Heaslip, M.A.Sc., P.Eng., has been investigating accidents since 1964. He has vast experience in all facets of the investigation process. Terry's expertise is evident throughout this book, but particularly in the interpretations of "witness mark" evidence on the recovered wreckage pieces.

Elaine Summers, who is an Aircraft Maintenance Engineer, started her investigation career with the TSB in 1988. She is a specialist in both on-site wreckage inspection, and laboratory wreckage analysis. In determining what led to the loss of an airplane, there is no substitute for years of actual on-site, hands-on accident investigation experience.

My accident investigation career started with the TSB in 1984, as an on-site field investigator. I have been investigator-in-charge for more than two hundred investigations, and have been directly involved in countless others. I have investigated high-profile cases around the world, and have benefited from interacting with, and learning from, some of the world's top investigation experts.

Ted Parisee, who did the graphics work for this book, has been involved in accident investigation since 1999. He specializes in the study of crash dynamics, and in presenting his findings in both graphic, and animated forms. Ted's son, Andrew Parisee, assisted him in preparing some of these graphics.

Collectively, we have well over one hundred years of continuous service in professional aviation accident investigation. We have investigated many aviation accidents that involved impact with water. In constructing this book, it was a tremendous advantage for me to have this collective wealth of experience to draw upon.

1

My motivation for writing this book was a long time coming. As I finish writing this in 2018, it has been four years since MH370 disappeared on 8 March 2014. It is now approaching three years since the first piece of wreckage from MH370 (the flaperon) was discovered in July 2015.

In August 2016, I provided my opinions about MH370 to *60 Minutes Australia*, and those opinions went worldwide in the media. If you have interest, you can check that out on my website.

As I stated in that *60 Minutes* interview, and have stated in other media, I firmly believed that the evidence on the recovered flaperon would guide the official investigators to what caused the disappearance of MH370. I thought they would examine the evidence on that recovered flaperon, and on the subsequently discovered section of outboard flap, and quickly conclude that MH370 ended its flight with the flaps fully extended (down) during a pilot controlled ditching. Clearly, it was an MH370 pilot who caused MH370 to disappear.

To my great surprise, and I must admit professional disappointment, the official investigation did not come to that conclusion. Instead, they continued to support their theory of an unpiloted airplane. Their belief is that MH370 entered the ocean unpiloted, while in a high-speed diving crash. That belief is simply not true, and the evidence against it is overwhelming.

As a sideline to our investigation work, we also teach accident investigation courses. In our courses, we use the evidence from MH370 to explain how to find and interpret evidence on wreckage pieces. We teach investigators how to apply basic investigation logic, and to reach conclusions based on solid evidence.

The physical evidence you will be exposed to about MH370 is not new. It has been available for a long time, to those who are capable of seeing and understanding it. Through the media, and some unofficial contacts, I have encouraged the official investigation to open their eyes to the obvious evidence on the recovered wreckage pieces. Those initiatives have not succeeded.

In the past months, I have come to realize that it is unlikely the physical evidence presented here will come to public knowledge through any source other than directly from me. In particular, I am now convinced it will not come from the official investigation. They have had ample opportunity, but have remained steadfast in their inaccurate thinking. I expect they will modify their opinions soon after they see and understand the irrefutable evidence presented here.

I was also motivated by a desire to counter other accounts of what happened to MH370. Much of what has been written in books and articles and other accounts is inaccurate. Some of it is outright shameful, and an insult to those who perished in this tragic event, and to their families and loved ones.

It is bad enough when people with no particular investigation expertise publicly present unsupported and illogical theories. It is even worse when people who have an actual aviation connection put forth ill-informed analysis. I believe

2

that when you have finished reading this account of what actually happened, you will be able to make your own good judgement as to who provided valid and helpful information.

Prior to writing this, my public writing experience has been in the production of professional accident investigation reports. That work involves technical writing that can be very detailed and focused. To fully understand the complexities of such technical writing might require some related technical knowledge.

Here, I have tried my best to write for a much wider audience. Fortunately, the physical evidence that is necessary to understand what happened to MH370 is not overly complicated. As you will see, it can be explained in relatively simple terms, and supported by photos of the actual wreckage pieces that are clear and very demonstrative.

The physical evidence revealed here is believable and convincing because you can clearly see it for yourself. Hopefully, I have met my objective to explain this evidence using plain language that anyone can understand.

To understand the full MH370 event, we must address not only what happened, but also why it happened. Why would the pilot intentionally take the airplane to a place where he knew there could be no survival? I will offer my thoughts on what the evidence reveals about the pilot's motivation, and where specialists in human behaviour should look for more answers.

This account of what happened to MH370 describes the events up to and including the entry of the airplane into the water. I am aware of how such descriptions can be upsetting, especially to those who had family and loved ones on board. When I was an accident investigator for the Canadian government, part of my obligation was to interact with those who were left to grieve.

In these interactions, many of them would look for indications of what it was like for their loved ones in the airplane. Inevitably, many would focus their questions on – what did they see, what did they feel, what was their anxiety level, what was their state of awareness about what was happening, or about to happen – in other words, were they scared, and did they suffer. These were never easy conversations, but invariably the feedback I got was that the information they received was helpful and appreciated.

For MH370, there is no way to be certain whether the people in the airplane were conscious, or even alive, through to the end of the flight. However, I believe that the scenario that best fits with the intentions and planning of the pilot would be for him to have depressurized the airplane shortly after he disabled the electronic tracking. Depressurization would be one of the very first non-routine events, some forty minutes into the flight. The depressurization would have been the only traumatic event the occupants would have experienced, as they would have very quickly lost consciousness, or succumbed, due to hypoxia.

3

I believe that the pilot was the only person on board MH370 who was cognisant of what was happening when the airplane was southbound over the ocean, and when he ditched the airplane on the ocean surface at the end of its flight. In all of the evidence presented here, there is nothing that contradicts this most likely scenario.

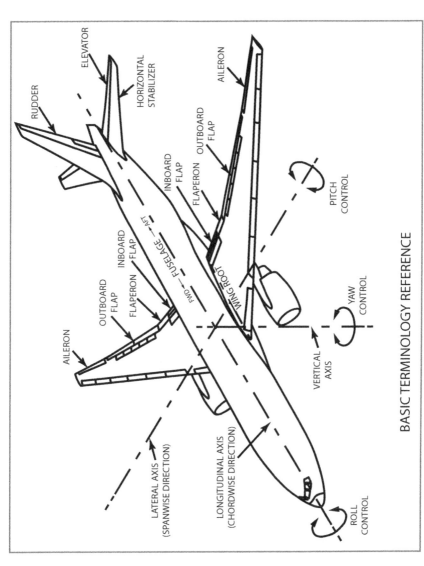

RUDDER

ELEVATOR

HORIZONTAL STABILIZER

AILERON

OUTBOARD FLAP

INBOARD FLAP

FLAPERON

FUSELAGE

AFT

FWD

WING ROOT

PITCH CONTROL

YAW CONTROL

VERTICAL AXIS

AILERON

OUTBOARD FLAP

FLAPERON

INBOARD FLAP

LATERAL AXIS (SPANWISE DIRECTION)

LONGITUDINAL AXIS (CHORDWISE DIRECTION)

ROLL CONTROL

BASIC TERMINOLOGY REFERENCE

FIGURE 1 Boeing 777 Reference Diagram

1
INTRODUCTION

The disappearance of MH370 is widely viewed as one of the greatest mysteries in the history of aviation. What could cause a huge passenger airplane to simply disappear into the night? Evidence shows that MH370 flew to the southern Indian Ocean, and that it is now resting at the bottom of the sea.

When the investigation authorities suspended the official search for MH370 on 17 January 2017, after nearly three years of searching, many people were disappointed by the lack of definitive answers as to what caused the airplane to disappear. The hope for answers was renewed when a privately funded search for wreckage was restarted in January 2018. Once more, the renewed search has failed to find the wreckage.

The uncertainty as to what happened to MH370 has left room for outside experts to fill the void with differing theories and viewpoints. Most of these outside experts have little or no experience in actual airplane accident investigation.

The searches for the wreckage of MH370 were based on a belief by the investigation authorities that for more than six hours the airplane was tracking to the southern Indian Ocean as an unpiloted airplane. Their belief has been that during that time, MH370 was flying on autopilot, without pilot input, and that it eventually ran out of fuel. They believe that at the end of its flight MH370 entered an out-of-control high-speed descent, followed by a high-speed crash into the ocean.

The evidence that I will present proves that the unpiloted airplane theory is not correct. The airplane did not dive at high speed into the ocean. Basic investigation techniques substantiate a very different scenario: the disappearance of MH370 was a man-made event. The evidence shows that the airplane was under the complete control of a pilot throughout the flight, and at the end of its flight, MH370 was intentionally ditched (landed in a controlled way) on the ocean surface.

The disappearance of MH370 was a deliberate, pre-planned act, conducted by a pilot who followed the exact sequence of events that he intended to follow. The pilot's intention was to fly the airplane to a pre-determined remote location in the southern Indian Ocean, and to ditch the airplane in such a way that it would remain intact, and to cause the airplane to sink to the depths of the ocean without leaving a trace.

Had the pilot's plan worked out exactly as he intended, the disappearance of MH370 would indeed have remained as one of the world's great mysteries. It would not have been possible to determine where the airplane went, or to determine how the flight ended.

Fortunately, there were two shortcomings in his planning, and because of these two shortcomings, evidence was left behind about what happened. First, the pilot was unaware that he could not disable the airplane's systems in such a way as to make the airplane completely disappear from all electronic tracking. Second, he did not anticipate that pieces of the airplane would be dislodged during the controlled ditching, and that the dislodged pieces would be sufficiently buoyant to float until they reached the shoreline.

The evidence to support a deliberate act is very clear. I will explain how a basic and logical step-by-step investigation process can be used to uncover and analyze the evidence. For example, you will see proof that as it approached and entered the water at the end of its flight, the airplane was flying with its wings level – they were not tilted to either side. The airplane was in a landing attitude, with its nose pitched slightly up. It was flying at a normal landing speed, and ready for a controlled ditching on the ocean surface.

You will see how the damage patterns on two recovered wreckage pieces (the right flaperon, and a section of the right outboard flap) prove that the landing flaps were extended (down) when the airplane settled into the water. You will understand the significance of the landing flaps being extended – how the flaps could not have been extended unless a pilot intentionally selected them to the extended position. By understanding the available evidence, you will see that at the end of its flight, MH370 was being flown by a pilot who was intentionally executing a controlled ditching.

You will also see that through the use of standard investigation techniques, and simple reasoning, other theories can be dismissed, including the high-speed-dive theory supported by the official investigation.

Why Did the Official Investigation Get It Wrong?

An obvious question here would be: if the evidence is so clear to support the pilot-controlled ditching theory, and to dismiss the high-speed-dive theory, why did the official investigation get it wrong? There is no easy answer to that question. I will address it in greater detail later, but I offer the following here.

In the early part of the official investigation, they discovered that (despite his best efforts) the pilot had not completely cut off all electronic communication

8

with the airplane. The airplane continued to have automatic hourly contact with a satellite. That electronic contact left behind data that was used by the official investigation to reconstruct the airplane's basic flight path. The official investigation became focused on the satellite data, looking for clues about where to search for wreckage.

Over time, the official investigation used the satellite data to (mistakenly) conclude that during its flight southbound, MH370 had flown without a functioning pilot. Their assumption was that the airplane flew at a normal cruising altitude until it ran out of fuel. They then used their calculated location for fuel exhaustion as a starting point from which to develop their search area coordinates.

The unpiloted airplane scenario became entrenched in the collective thinking. Later on, as the evidence from damage patterns on the recovered wreckage pieces became available, that evidence was either overlooked, or misinterpreted. It seems the investigators simply lacked the specific expertise required to correctly identify and interpret that evidence.

It appears that throughout the official investigation, the energy and focus was on the work of the people interpreting the satellite-related data. It appears that the intensity of this work, and the passion and world-class expertise of those engaged in it, pulled the focus of the investigation in that direction, and away from the basic wreckage analysis investigation.

The Disappearance of MH370 Was A Deliberate Act

From the very start, the overriding question in the disappearance of MH370 was whether it could be a deliberate act by one of the pilots. In my view, right from the beginning the evidence pointed in that direction. Later, I will explain this in detail, but the basics are this: the first known anomaly was the disappearance of the electronic radar signal from the airplane (the transponder signal); the transponder signal was lost as the result of a lead event; the lead event being whatever caused the transponder signal to disappear.

The disappearance of the transponder signal (the first known anomaly) was either a technical failure event, or it was a deliberate act. The basic follow-on anomalies included the complete loss of radio contact with the pilots, the loss of routine (automatic) electronic messaging from the airplane, the changing track of the airplane, and the long flight south over the ocean. From a logical investigation perspective, this sequence by itself placed the likelihood of this being a technical failure event at low, and the likelihood of it being a deliberate act at high.

The turning point for the official investigation, away from the unpiloted airplane theory and toward the deliberate act theory, should have come on 29 July 2015 with the discovery of the flaperon from the right wing. The physical evidence available from examining the flaperon should have proven to the official investigation that the aircraft's flaps were extended (down) when it entered the water, and that the airplane was at a speed consistent with a pilot-controlled ditching.

After the recovery of the flaperon, there should have remained little doubt that a pilot was controlling MH370 at the end of its flight. Subsequent wreckage discoveries, and in particular a section from the right outboard flap that was found on 10 May 2016, should have added to the level of confidence that this event was a pilot-controlled ditching.

In fact, as you will see, the evidence from all twenty recovered wreckage pieces from MH370 confirm this was a controlled ditching event, and yet the official investigation continued to support their conclusion that MH370 was an unpiloted airplane.

Accident vs. Intentional Criminal Act

Aircraft accidents almost never result from a single cause. A typical accident investigation requires complex analysis. Accident reports contain detailed explanations involving long chains of events which point to and support multiple findings and causes. A successful accident investigation results in recommendations for accident prevention.

The investigation into the disappearance of MH370 is different, because MH370 was not an accident. MH370 has only one cause. It was caused by an intentional criminal act, perpetrated by one individual. There is no complex sequence of failures like there would be in an accident scenario. MH370 can be explained by one single cause, that being the conduct of the pilot.

The simplicity of the disappearance of MH370 comes down to this: either it was a criminal act, or it was not. Either MH370 was caused by some technical event, which would indeed make it an exceptionally complicated accident with a complicated chain of events, or MH370 was a man-made event – a devious but simple criminal act, with no complicated chain of events to unravel.

The evidence confirms it was a criminal act, committed by one individual who, as a pilot in the airplane, had a simple means to carry it out. There was nothing to prevent an MH370 pilot from commandeering his own airplane, and then following the exact sequence of events that eventually took the airplane to the bottom of the ocean. That is what happened, and that is a fact.

2
ADDRESSING
SPECIFIC READERS

Families and Loved Ones

My career as a government safety board investigator gave me the opportunity to engage in many interactions with grieving families and loved ones, both in the immediate aftermath of an accident, and on a longer-term basis. In my investigation courses, I teach family relations, and in particular the necessity to keep the needs of families at the forefront during the investigation process.

I expect there will be family members who will be thankful to have the information presented here. There may be others who will be upset, and non-accepting of the evidence. My experience with families has been that if the evidence is compelling, and clearly presented, they will be able to assess all the information and come to accurate conclusions. In such tragic circumstances, it is always best that those who have suffered the loss of loved ones have an opportunity to understand the facts, and come to recognize the truth.

In interacting with families, my advice to them has always been to be sceptical of information and analysis that comes from sources outside the official investigation. I recognize that I am an outside source. I have had no inside exposure to the official MH370 investigation. However, my investigation partners and I have decades of relevant experience to draw upon, and we are confident that what is presented here is correct.

Professional Accident Investigators

Hopefully, readers will include professional aircraft accident investigators. Those who work for government accident investigation agencies are also known as air safety investigators. They investigate for the purpose of accident prevention. For major investigations, they work as a team. The official investigation brings in whatever outside help is necessary to ensure they have sufficient expertise to produce a successful outcome.

Airplane accident investigation has become increasingly reliant on high-tech electronic data collection. The collection devices, such as flight data recorders, have been mainstays in accident investigation for decades. Data collection and monitoring is becoming increasingly sophisticated and effective. This provides investigators with increased insight about what was happening with the airplane in the timeframe leading up to the accident.

Unfortunately, the increased reliance on electronic data has come at a cost. There is a worrying decrease in the capability of investigators to think analytically while assessing all the available evidence. In particular, there has been a marked drop-off in their ability to interpret basic wreckage damage patterns. There is less focus on the markings that are left on wreckage pieces from impacts with each other, or with whatever else they might have struck during the impact.

The marks (such as scratches, dents, abrasions, etc.) that are left from such impacts are called "witness marks", because they can reveal much about the pre-impact state of the airplane. For example, you can line up witness marks on wreckage pieces to reveal the position of flight controls at the time of impact. Such information can be vital in determining what was happening with the airplane prior to impact. Experienced investigators know that it is important for basic wreckage analysis to remain as the starting point for a thorough investigation.

The sophistication of electronic surveillance will evolve, and investigators will be drawn to that. However, investigators must also remember that very solid evidence can be available from wreckage analysis. It is important for investigation agencies to be able to assess witness marks using the basic laws of physics. Investigators must recognize that the laws of physics do not change, regardless of their level of confidence in the electronic data.

The MH370 investigation went down the wrong path because of an over-reliance on high tech investigation efforts, and the inability to properly interpret the witness marks on the recovered wreckage pieces.

Perhaps some investigators who worked on the MH370 investigation will read this account of what happened. From first-hand experience, I am well aware of the level of intensity they experienced during this high-profile investigation. Having looked at what they produced, I have great respect for their level of effort. Some of the techniques they developed were groundbreaking, and future investigations will benefit from these enhanced capabilities.

For example, I have great respect for the expertise that was used to determine the southerly track line. Equally impressive was the expertise employed to plan and complete the underwater searches. This was world-class work. Later, we will see how it was based on some incorrect assumptions, but that does not take away from the impressive expertise involved.

By reviewing the publicly available documentation gathered during the investigation (what we call tombstone data), it is obvious that investigators in Malaysia and elsewhere spent countless hours putting it all together. This is vital work, and in my view it all appears to be well done.

Despite these good efforts, the investigators failed to properly assess the available evidence that should have informed them they were not dealing with an unpiloted airplane. The most glaring failure was in the primary task of conducting proper wreckage analysis.

It is evident that the wreckage analysis evidence was either overlooked, or misinterpreted. Because of that, the incorrect theory of the unpiloted airplane became the primary influence over much of the investigation decision-making, especially for resource allocation in the search for wreckage. I will address these topics in more detail in later chapters.

Spokespeople for the Official MH370 Investigation

Perhaps the audience for this book will include the spokespeople for the Official MH370 investigation, those who took responsibility for presenting information to the public. Like most people around the world, I followed the information release aspect of the MH370 investigation from afar.

On other major investigations, I have been involved in preparations for the public release of information, so I know how difficult it can be to strike the right balance as the investigation progresses, especially when there is a lack of definitive information about what actually happened. It is the responsibility of the official investigation to be transparent and informative, but they are constrained by the protocol to release only confirmed factual information. They must also be aware of evidence protection requirements for any potential criminal investigation.

In assessing the dynamic between the MH370 investigation authorities, and those demanding information from them, it was my opinion that much of the criticism directed at the Malaysian response early in the investigation was unfair. I tried to imagine how it would have been different in any positive way if this had been a British airplane that departed London, or a French airplane that departed Paris, or an American airplane that departed New York.

Given the mysterious circumstance of the airplane's disappearance, and the lack of information about what happened to it, there is no reason to believe that the criticisms and commentary would have been much different no matter who was in charge.

That is not to say that improvements could not have been made. All major investigations provide opportunities to learn from what happened, and to better prepare for the next event. There are lessons that can be taken from how MH370 was handled from a communications perspective.

I believe the Malaysian authorities could have done more to strive for public trust and confidence in the investigation. Public trust comes from showing professionalism, independence, openness, competence, organization, and cooperation between agencies. All preparation and training for occurrence investigations must recognize the need to meet these requirements.

During the official investigation's search for the MH370 wreckage, there was one particular and surprising misstep that stood out to me, and it negatively affected the credibility of the investigation. A spokesperson for the investigation proclaimed, and with a high degree of confidence, that the flight path calculations based on the satellite data were accurate, and that based on those calculations the wreckage site would soon be found.

Basic media training emphasizes that during an ongoing investigation you never make such a promise of results. Public confidence is lost when promised results are not delivered. The proper promise is a promise of effort, because that is a promise that can be kept.

The spokespeople did make some very appropriate promises. For example, they promised to employ every resource available in their search for the airplane. They also promised to ensure full coverage in their searches of the most likely areas. These promises were fulfilled, but the positive publicity they generated was overshadowed by the unfulfilled promise to find the airplane.

In the lead-up to the major new search initiative that started in January 2018, there were many instances where some of those associated with determining where to look for wreckage used language that heightened the expectations of success. They spoke of using new research and analysis, which allowed them to zero in on likely crash sites. They spoke of how this gave them great confidence that the airplane wreckage would be found, and found quickly.

As will be detailed later, like the promises made during the official search, these promises of results never had a realistic chance of being realized. Again, the new search was reliant on the incorrect assumption of an unpiloted airplane, and this incorrect assumption was a major contributor in the calculations for their search zones.

Members of the Media, and Expert Commentators

The audience for this book may include members of the media who covered MH370. Understandably, the disappearance of MH370 generated worldwide round-the-clock coverage. The interest level remained high for a long time, with attention given to any new information or analysis, from whatever source.

Like many others, in the aftermath of the airplane's disappearance I followed the media coverage. I am always amazed at how quickly information can start to flow. Initially, there was some very informative coverage about what had happened. There was good reporting about the investigation processes, and the search for wreckage, and the operation of the Boeing 777.

Then, as inevitably happens, the media coverage started to turn more toward speculation. Much of this commentary was from people who have never done actual investigation work. In my opinion, it is disrespectful to professional investigators, and unfair to the audience, when so-called experts present themselves as actual experienced investigators when in fact they are not.

It is particularly disturbing when people who so clearly lack expertise or sound logic are encouraged by media hosts to offer up their best guesses about what happened. I know from personal experience how much grief and stress such messaging can bring to families who have no way to filter out fact from fiction.

Those who engage in this, both on the media side, and on the experts side, should be aware of the harm they can cause. I have seen it first hand; exposure to such misinformation can push vulnerable people into an increased state of stress, and it is not ethical to be a participant in that type of activity.

Hobbyist Investigators

Perhaps the readers of this book will include what I will call hobbyist investigators. As has happened with other high-profile investigations, some people have become engrossed in the intrigue associated with the disappearance of MH370. If you do an internet search, you can find numerous theories, from any number of sources, speculating about what happened.

I have looked at only a small portion of what seems to be available. There are people who have put countless hours into researching all facets of the MH370 disappearance. People dig into every aspect of analysis and causation, and put their thoughts forward. Other people throw their opinions into the mix. Conspiracy theories are rampant.

There are many people who are convinced that the only sensible answer to the mystery of MH370 is that an MH370 pilot must have been involved. This account of what happened will provide them with the proof they need to show that they were correct.

In my cursory looks, I have come across some writings that are amazingly detailed, particularly from those who support the unpiloted airplane theory. In some cases, it is obvious that the authors are highly skilled, and highly motivated, and eager to share their abundant intelligence.

Their research and contributions certainly add to the overall knowledge base. Their conclusions are based on the facts as they see them, and would be of great significance to the investigation if only they were correct.

Perhaps the solid evidence presented here will motivate them to look at their evidence from the perspective that there was no unpiloted airplane. This would give them a more solid base from which to continue their discussions.

3

FACTUAL INFORMATION FROM OFFICIAL REPORTS

Any investigation starts from the known facts. In the case of MH370, the basic facts surrounding the flight were produced by the official investigation, which included experts from Malaysia, Australia, China, United Kingdom, United States and France.

I have extracted the factual information included here from documents released by the official investigation. I refer specifically to documents from the following two agencies: *The Malaysian ICAO Annex 13 Safety Investigation Team for MH370*, and the *Australian Transport Safety Bureau* (ATSB).

During any investigation, it can be difficult to agree on what actually constitutes a "fact". However, I agree with the following basic facts that, as mentioned, originated with the official investigation.

MH370 – Confirmed Flight History

Malaysia Airlines Flight 370 (MH370) was a Boeing 777-200ER (B777) airplane that departed Kuala Lumpur International Airport in the dark of night, at 42 minutes past midnight local time on 8 March 2014. The destination was Beijing, China. On board were 12 Malaysian crewmembers, and 227 passengers.

The captain of the airplane was Zaharie Ahmad Shah, who was 53 years old. He was married and had three children. Captain Shah had been an airline pilot with Malaysia Airlines for 33 years, and had 18,423 hours of flight time. He had been a B777 captain for 16 years, and had 8,659 hours on that airplane type. By virtue of his good track record and seniority, he had been designated as a Type Rating Instructor, and Type Rating Examiner, on the B777. He was recognized as an accomplished and well-respected pilot who had no blemishes on his record.

The co-pilot of the airplane was Fariq Abdul Hamid, who was 27 years old. He was unmarried. Co-pilot Hamid had been an airline pilot with Malaysia Airlines for 7 years, and had 2,813 hours of flight time. He was in the process of transitioning to the B777, and was just finishing his mandatory training to complete the transition. He had 39 hours on the B777. MH370 was to be his final training flight prior to undergoing his "check ride", which was to take place on his next scheduled flight. This type-check training is a normal process in airline operations. Captain Shah, as a designated Type Rating Instructor, was authorized to conduct such training on regularly scheduled flights.

The planned flight duration for MH370 was 5 hours, 34 minutes. The captain had ordered sufficient fuel for a flight endurance of 7 hours, 31 minutes, allowing some two hours of contingency fuel.

The flight departed normally from Kuala Lumpur, and climbed to its planned cruising altitude of Flight Level 350 (written as "FL350", which is approximately 35,000 feet above sea level). It proceeded toward its first en route electronic waypoint – the IGARI waypoint. (Airplanes navigate along an assigned route by tracking through a series of fixed locations, known as waypoints, which provide a more-or-less straight-line track to their destination.)

About 37 minutes after departure, as the airplane was approaching the IGARI waypoint, Air Traffic Control (ATC) cleared MH370 to switch to the communication radio frequency of the next control sector, where the pilot would be expected to report in.

In the area of the IGARI waypoint, the airplane was in a transition zone. It would leave the airspace controlled by the Kuala Lumpur ATC sector, and enter the airspace controlled by the Ho Chi Minh ATC sector. The reply from the airplane to Kuala Lumpur ATC was, "Good night Malaysia Three Seven Zero". As has been well documented, this was the final radio communication with MH370.

Less than two minutes after that final radio transmission, a significant anomaly occurred on board MH370. Something happened on board the airplane that caused the airplane to disappear from all ATC radar screens. The electronic tracking signal from the airplane completely disappeared. This electronic signal is transmitted from the airplane by a radio unit called a transponder. The transponder signal is sent in response to an interrogation from a ground-based radar facility. After the transponder signal disappeared from the radar screens, MH370 was essentially invisible to ATC.

From that point on, after the transponder signal disappeared, there was no more ATC interaction with MH370. There was no more voice communication with the airplane, and MH370 was no longer under any ATC control or monitoring.

Initially, the disappearance of MH370 did not raise any red flags with the controllers at ATC. This was because of the specific location where the transponder signal disappeared from the radar screens – just as the flight was being handed off from one control sector to the next. Investigators found that it had taken some time before the controller in the receiving sector noticed that an expected airplane (MH370) had not checked in, or shown up on his radar screen.

I have added the following commentary for context, and not to provide an excuse for ATC. A receiving controller is not necessarily focused on watching the radar screen for a handed-off airplane to show up. Their primary responsibility is collision avoidance. ATC's task is to ensure the track and altitude of the incoming airplane (MH370) do not conflict with another airplane in their sector. A receiving controller would know that the clearance delivery system would not have issued the assigned track and altitude for MH370 to enter their sector if a potential conflict existed. Also, there would be an expectation by the receiving controller that any airplane entering their sector would immediately check in, thereby drawing their attention. Most certainly the MH370 pilot would be aware of this dynamic, and that is why he chose this specific location to make his airplane disappear.

Essentially, at 01:21 local time (39 minutes after departure) MH370 simply disappeared. It was only after some 17 minutes that the Ho Chi Minh ATC sector controller noticed that MH370 had not checked in, and that sector checked with the Kuala Lumpur ATC sector to see what might have gone wrong. The Kuala Lumpur ATC sector contacted the other ATC sectors along the flight-planned route, but none of them had established contact with MH370.

It was not until some 5 hours after MH370 had disappeared from electronic radar tracking that the Kuala Lumpur Rescue Coordination Centre was activated, and a search-and-rescue operation was initiated. ATC could not provide the Rescue Coordination Centre with any specific information about the whereabouts of the flight, other than where it was when it disappeared. They had no way of knowing whether MH370 had landed, or crashed, or had flown on in some unknown direction.

Over time, investigation officials learned more about the history of the flight. In the days following the disappearance of the MH370, investigators studied recorded radar from a number of different radar sources, looking for primary radar returns they could attribute to the airplane. They discovered that after MH370 disappeared (electronically) from the civilian ATC radar screens near the IGARI waypoint, it had remained visible (as a primary radar return only) on some military radar screens.

From studying these primary radar returns, they discovered that almost immediately after crossing the IGARI waypoint, and at virtually the same time as the transponder signal disappeared, MH370 diverted completely away from its original flight plan. Instead of following its expected course straight ahead towards its destination, it first made a slight right turn, and then an immediate and aggressive left turn to basically reverse course.

19

Investigators found that MH370 then followed an unexpected track that took it first to the southwest, to near Penang Island, and then to the west over the Andaman Sea north of Indonesia. The specific track followed by MH370, along the borderlines between radar stations, kept the airplane from attracting the attention of a number of military radar installations.

Even after MH370 flew out of radar range, investigators were able to determine a basic track line for the airplane. Led by the ATSB, investigators were able to use satellite communication signals transmitted from the airplane to determine that after passing the northern tip of Sumatra (Indonesia), MH370 turned to the south and flew for some six hours in a southerly direction. They calculated that the airplane ended its flight in the southern Indian Ocean, west of Australia.

By digging further into the records, investigators discovered another anomaly that had occurred early in the flight of MH370. They found that there had been an unexpected loss of communication between the airplane's ACARS system (Aircraft Communications Addressing and Reporting System) and the satellite it was communicating through.

ACARS works in the background to provide a platform for routine messaging with the airplane. At specific intervals, ACARS is also used to automatically send out routine status reports from the airplane. Reports can be sent to the airline, and to the engine manufacturers, and to others. The ACARS reports contain information about the functioning of certain monitored systems, including the engines.

Unlike the transponder signal, it was not possible for the investigators to determine an exact time for when the ACARS was disrupted. That is because unlike the transponder, the ACARS transmissions occur only intermittently. On MH370, the routine scheduled transmissions were to occur every 30 minutes.

Investigators discovered that the last successful routine (scheduled) ACARS transmission from MH370 occurred 25 minutes after departure, 14 minutes prior to the disappearance of the transponder signal. The next routine (scheduled) ACARS transmission was not received. Investigators could then conclude that the disruption to ACARS happened sometime during that 30 minutes, within the same timeframe that the electronic transponder signal was lost.

To put context to this information about ACARS, you will see that it is my contention that the pilot intentionally turned off the transponder, and intentionally tried to disable the ACARS functioning. He took both actions in a relatively short timeframe. Fortunately, the pilot was not aware that he did not disable one specific ACARS/satellite connection to do with engine monitoring. It was this remaining electronic connection with the satellite that investigators used to figure out that the airplane had flown to the southern Indian Ocean. For those who are familiar with the term, it was this connection that produced the "handshakes" – there will be much more on this later.

Unlike the transponder signal, which is critical because it lets ATC know where the airplane is, the dropout of ACARS would not be noticeable to anybody straight away.

As stated previously, the above factual information is consistent with that released by the official investigation. I accept it as being credible.

4
EXAMINING
THE PHYSICAL EVIDENCE

We will now transition to looking at the evidence that proves the pilot intentionally ditched MH370 on the ocean surface. As I stated earlier, the evidence is clear and persuasive, and you can see it for yourself in the included photographs of the wreckage pieces. As you read on, I believe you will come to understand every aspect of what happened, and have a full appreciation for the amount of evidence that confirms the airplane's flaps were extended (down) during a pilot-controlled ditching.

Information About Floating Debris

First, I would like to put some context to the scenario supported by the official investigation, which is a high-speed diving crash into the water. I have significant first-hand experience looking at wreckage from that type of event.

If MH370 had experienced a high-speed diving crash, it would have produced tens of thousands of pieces of floating debris. Some of the initial floating debris would become non-buoyant over time, and it would sink to the ocean bottom before it could reach a coastline. It is also a fact that some significant amount of the floating debris would remain buoyant for a very long time.

Only some twenty pieces of wreckage confirmed to be from MH370 have been recovered to date. Each recovered piece had drifted to the east coast of Africa, far away from where the airplane had entered the ocean. Most of these pieces had remained buoyant because of the honeycomb materials used in their construction. A high-speed diving crash would have created at least hundreds of additional wreckage pieces with honeycomb type construction. Had they actually been created, many more than twenty pieces would have already been discovered.

A high-speed diving crash would have created many pieces of other types of floating debris, including seat cushions, luggage pieces, clothing, life jackets, personal effects, neck pillows, etc. The wreckage field from a high-speed diving crash would contain countless items that would remain buoyant for a long time. Had they actually been created, we would have seen this type of debris arriving on the coast of Africa in significant amounts.

A reasonable conclusion would be as follows: if there had been a high-speed diving crash, many more than twenty pieces of floating debris would have followed a comparable path to the coast of Africa. The reason that more floating debris has not appeared is that it was never created in the first place. There was no high-speed diving crash.

Our Wreckage Examination Process

In our search for evidence to produce this account of the facts, we did not have access to the actual wreckage pieces. However, we did have access to high-resolution photos of the wreckage pieces that showed us all the evidence necessary to draw our conclusions.

We looked for evidence that could reveal the airplane's speed, attitude (flight angle) and flap configuration as it approached the water surface. This is the type of evidence needed to determine if there was a high-speed diving crash, or if there was a pilot-controlled ditching. We looked closely at each piece of recovered debris to determine exactly how it became dislodged as the airplane entered the water.

As stated earlier, all the evidence points to a relatively low-speed, pilot-controlled ditching on the ocean surface. There is no evidence of a high-speed diving crash. In fact, there is overwhelming evidence to contradict that scenario.

I do not want to imply that ditching a B777 on the ocean is a low-energy event, but it is important to understand the exponential difference in energy between a relatively low-speed controlled ditching, and a high-speed diving crash. Damage wise, there is no comparison between the two.

In a relatively low-speed controlled ditching, the airplane will take a number of seconds to come to a stop. There will be damage, but the airplane structure can survive relatively intact. In a high-speed diving crash, the energy levels are extreme, and the airplane is completely destroyed in a fraction of a second.

Swissair 111 was a McDonnell Douglas MD-11 airline airplane that crashed at high speed into the Atlantic Ocean off the coast of Canada in 1998. I was Deputy

FIGURE 2 Typical Wreckage Pieces from Swissair 111

24

Investigator-In-Charge of that investigation. Figure 2 illustrates the extent of the damage that occurred when hydrodynamic multi-axial forces destroyed that MD-11 airplane in a fraction of a second.

Figure 2 shows representative wreckage pieces from Swissair 111. In this photo, there are hundreds, or even thousands, of individual pieces of airplane structure that were recovered from the ocean bottom. The wreckage pieces are shown on the primary sorting table, where each individual piece of wreckage was examined for investigation evidence. This examination process, which looked at some two million pieces, was ongoing for some fifteen months. These pieces of wreckage are representative of the type of destruction that would have been inflicted on MH370 if there had been a high-speed diving crash.

Examination of the Recovered MH370 Flaperon

The earliest physical evidence that MH370 entered the water during a pilot-controlled ditching came with the recovery of the flaperon from the right wing. Figure 3 shows the in-service location of the flaperons. There is one flaperon on each wing. In Figure 3, one view shows the flaperon in its streamlined (up) position, and the other view shows it in its fully deflected (down) position.

The flaperons are part of the flight control system, helping the ailerons and spoilers to control the rolling movements of the airplane. For example, the flaperons can deflect up or down to help roll the airplane into or out of a turn, or to keep the wings level during turbulence.

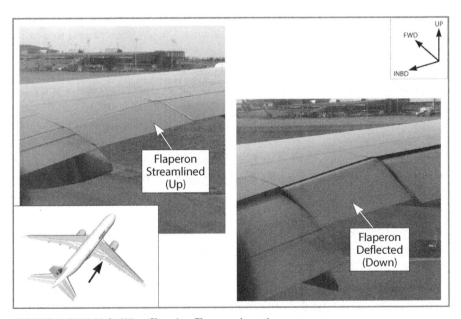

FIGURE 3 B777 Right Wing Showing Flaperon Location

25

For take off and landing, the flaperons also function as part of the flap system. They deflect down when the pilot selects the flaps to "down". In normal circumstances, the flaps are partially extended (down) for take off, and fully extended (down) for landing. They are fully retracted (up) during cruise flight.

Figure 4 shows the recovered flaperon from the right wing of MH370.

Essentially, it was the entire right-wing flaperon that was recovered. For a size perspective, the recovered flaperon is about 8 feet (2.43 meters) long and about 5 feet (1.5 meters) wide, and it weighs about 110 pounds (50 kilograms). The view in Figure 4 is showing the leading edge, and the outboard end (the end farthest from the fuselage).

The skin and internal structural pieces of the flaperon are made primarily of composite materials. The skin is bonded to a honeycomb core. The flaperon is attached to the wing's rear spar by two hydraulic actuators that move it up and down, and two hinge-point connectors.

The official investigation contends that when MH370 struck the water in a high-speed diving crash, this flaperon was in its fully up position; that is, it was tucked neatly into the trailing edge of the wing, with no downward deflection (see Figure 3).

This is where we will start our first basic investigation analysis to assess the likelihood of a high-speed diving crash. We will start by observing the general condition of this flaperon.

We see that this recovered flaperon has maintained its basic structural integrity, and that it broke free from the back of the right wing as one piece. This recovered piece is basically the entire flaperon, but without the attachments that would have held it to the back of the wing – it has been ripped free of its attachments.

We see that it has retained its normal curved shape along its leading edge. It has also retained the normal curvature along its upper and lower surfaces. It presents itself as being not deformed, or flattened, or squashed, or even dented. There is damage where it was ripped from its attachments, as would be expected.

There is significant damage at the trailing edge of this flaperon that is not visible in Figure 4. This trailing edge damage will be thoroughly analyzed later, and you will see proof that the trailing edge damage occurred during the pilot-controlled ditching.

In wreckage description terms, this recovered flaperon would be classified as nearly pristine, because it has no signs of impact damage to its aerodynamic surfaces.

Now let us consider what this piece would have been subjected to if it had been involved in a high-speed diving crash. Here are some basic mathematical calculations.

Leading Edge

INBD

FWD

UP

FIGURE 4 Recovered MH370 Flaperon

27

In the scenario proposed by the official investigation, MH370's airspeed when it struck the ocean would have been at least 380 knots (437 mph, 704 kph). If you want to use a higher airspeed (or even a lower one) you can do your own conversions, but 380 knots is quite conservative for an airplane that they contend was unpiloted and descending at a high and increasing rate of descent – 380 knots converts to 641 feet (195 meters) per second.

The length of a B777-200ER is 209 feet (63.7 meters). The calculation shows that at 641 feet per second, it would have taken 0.326 seconds for the entire 209-foot length of the airplane to impact the water surface. Put another way, hydrodynamic multi-axial forces would have destroyed the entire airplane, from nose to tail, in 1/3 of a second.

To help you get a sense of just how quick this is, a normal blink of an eye takes about 1/3 of a second (try blinking three times in succession – to blink three times takes about 1 second). So we can say without exaggeration that if MH370 actually hit the water while in a high-speed diving crash, it would have started and finished crashing into the water – from nose to tail – in the blink of an eye.

I am aware that some people find this hard to visualize, but the mathematics do not lie – that is exactly how long the entire impact would take. If you are trying to visualize and absorb this, you must also realize that no part of the airplane would slow down appreciably as the impact was occurring. In other words, the last part of the tail would strike the water at virtually the same speed that the nose did (641 feet per second).

In a crash like this, all of the momentum is forward. The tail of the airplane is trying to catch up with the nose, and it does not slow down appreciably because of the impact happening in front of it. Of course there will be a big splash happening, but in that 1/3 of a second (a blink of an eye), every part of the airplane will impact into the non-compressible water at 641 feet per second.

Let's do some more mathematics to illustrate how fast the impact would happen along the length of the airplane. Start with the tip of the nose hitting the water. The airplane would have to travel another 90 feet (27 meters) before the leading edge of the wing (in front of the flaperon) would strike the water. That would take 0.14 seconds (1/10 of a second).

The chord of the wing (the distance from leading edge to trailing edge) in front of the flaperon is about 25 feet (7.6 meters), so the entry of the wing into the water would take 0.04 seconds (4/100 of a second). At the end of that 4/100 of a second, the leading edge of the flaperon would impact the water travelling at 641 feet per second. We could go on, but I think the point is made.

Along with Figure 2, Figure 5 shows what wreckage looks like when there is a high-speed diving crash.

In Figure 5, the photo on the left shows wreckage as it was brought to the surface from the Swissair 111 debris field on the bottom of the ocean. The photo

FIGURE 5 Wreckage from Swissair 111

on the right shows how some two million fragmented pieces of wreckage were stored in more than 700 large boxes. This illustrates how a high-speed diving crash causes massive destruction and fragmentation of the aircraft's structure as it explodes from the inside out.

Now have another look at Figure 4 showing the recovered flaperon from MH370. Does it make any sense to you that the recovered flaperon could survive basically unscathed from an impact like that? Do you think it is reasonable for anyone to conclude that the flaperon could endure such an extreme impact and still look the way it does? There is only one obvious answer – no.

You do not have to be an experienced investigator to make that judgement about the condition of the recovered MH370 flaperon. The use of common sense provides the answer. To me, it is inconceivable that any investigator, or anyone who claims to have investigation expertise, would not automatically think their way through this, and do the calculations. They should realize that the high-speed diving crash theory supported by the official investigation simply does not make sense, based on this evidence alone.

I am aware that other theories have been put forth to explain why the flaperon from MH370 did not sustain impact damage. Some people contend that the flaperon had already fallen off the airplane before the airplane hit the water. That did not happen, and there is definitive evidence to prove it did not happen. You will see that evidence below.

Other people have suggested that the recovered flaperon might have been protected by the wing structure in front of it, thereby shielding it from impact damage. In a high-speed diving crash into water, that simply does not happen.

Figure 6 depicts a B777 in a high-speed dive just as its nose is striking the ocean surface.

When you think of a high-speed crash sequence, it is helpful to think in terms of stop-action milliseconds. For example, the airplane in Figure 6 is stopped at the moment its nose reached the water surface. Now, visualize it progressing for another fraction of a second, while travelling just a tiny bit further, and then another bit further, and so on. That is the only way you can

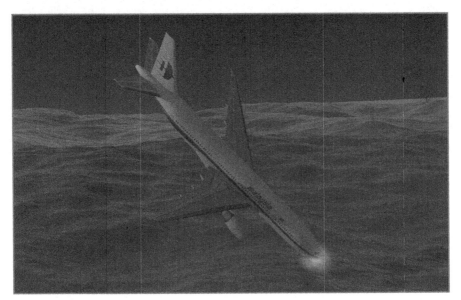

FIGURE 6 Depiction of a B777 in a High-Speed Diving Crash

visualize what will happen as the full length of a nose-down, 209-foot long airplane fully enters the water in 1/3 of a second.

In the high-speed diving crash scenario, the tip of the nose is the initial point of impact with the water surface; so again, visualize the airplane stopped there. The water is fluid, but it is not compressible. Now visualize moving a bit further into the water. The water exerts multi-axial forces starting at the very tip of the nose, and the nose starts to compress and fold in (rearward). There is insufficient structural support in the nose to resist the overwhelming force of the water, and the nose simply gives in.

As the airplane moves forward, the water instantly invades into the fuselage, which is basically a hollow cavity. An overwhelming pressure builds as the water invades up the fuselage, pushing from the inside of the fuselage out. The force of the invading water progresses up (into) the fuselage, pushing a pressure wave of compressed air ahead of it. As the pressure builds, the fuselage starts to rupture explosively from the inside out, from front to aft (front to back). The fuselage shatters and explodes outward, from the front all the way to the tail, creating countless numbers of pieces (as shown in the earlier photos from Swissair 111 – Figure 2 and Figure 5).

The same destructive sequence takes place with the wings, and flaps, and flaperons, which are all hollow cavities. The water forces would cause the leading edges of these structures to cave in and split open. The explosive rupture forces from the water would invade through the open leading edge, and rupture these pieces from the inside out.

To illustrate the destructive forces that are unleashed in a high-speed diving crash, I will share with you my experience from investigating the 1998 crash of Swissair 111.

From an impact perspective, that 1998 MD-11 crash would be comparable to what the official investigation has supported for MH370. When the Swissair MD-11 impacted the ocean surface at an estimated 300 knots (345 mph, 555 kph), which is 80 knots slower than what we have used for MH370, its hollow cavity structures ruptured explosively from the inside out as described above. The result was 285,000 pounds (129,273 kg) of airplane wreckage that had broken into some two million pieces (see Figure 2 and Figure 5).

I can also confirm for you that in the Swissair MD-11, the described hydro-dynamic forces were at play everywhere in the airplane. I include the following information not for dramatic effect, but rather to educate about the extreme destructive and invasive forces of water when high-speed impacts are involved. Inside the fuselage of Swissair 111, the hydrodynamic force of the water invaded into the skull cavities of the occupants, and the skulls were exploded from the inside out. This happened all the way from the front of the airplane to the back.

I believe that the pristine condition of the recovered flaperon from MH370 is sufficient all by itself to dismiss any support for the high-speed diving crash theory. However, there is much more evidence available to dismiss that theory, as you will see.

Now that we have made observations about the general condition of the re-covered right wing flaperon, let us turn to examining its trailing edge. Figure 7 shows the trailing edge (looking from the outboard end).

The flaperon is made primarily of composite material. We see at the trailing edge that it has been shredded away progressively, from the back towards the front. The original trailing edge is completely gone. It looks like it has been eaten away, or eroded. There is now a new and rather jagged trailing edge. In some places the erosion has progressed forward all the way to the rear spar that laterally stiffens the aft portion of the flaperon.

I have looked to see what the official investigation had to say about how this erosion happened. I cannot find where they have offered an opinion. One would think that such evidence would be an important element to their analy-sis, but it appears they have completely ignored it. Most certainly, this erosion damage does not fit in any way with their theory of a high-speed diving crash.

In a high-speed diving crash scenario, the flaps and flaperon would be fully up, which means they would be in a streamlined (trail) position, perfectly streamlined with the back of the wing (see Figure 3). If you imagine MH370 diving into the water (see Figure 6), do you think there is any plausible ex-planation for how the erosion we see at the trailing edge of the flaperon could

31

Trailing Edge Erosion

UP OUTBD
FWD

FIGURE 7 Showing the Flaperon Trailing Edge Erosion Damage

32

be created? The answer is no. In a high-speed dive scenario, there are no forces that could cause such erosion at the trailing edge.

Again, you do not have to be an experienced investigator to make that assessment. It is simply common sense. What would be the force that would cause it? How could that amount of erosion happen in a tiny fraction (4/100) of a second? If there had been a high-speed diving crash scenario, there is nothing about that erosion that makes any sense. In a high-speed diving crash scenario, the entire flaperon would have experienced an explosive rupture from the inside out, so there would be nothing left to erode.

It is not too difficult to envision how the trailing edge erosion on the recovered MH370 flaperon actually happened. Visualize the airplane in a controlled ditching configuration, flying just above the water surface, with the landing gear retracted (up), and the flaps extended (down). The airplane would be in a slightly nose up attitude, flying at about 140 knots (161 mph, 259 kph), and slowing down. It would be slowly descending, and about to touch the water surface. Figure 8 provides a visual depiction of what that would look like.

As depicted in Figure 8, the engines, which are mounted under the wings, would be the first to contact the water by touching the tops of the swells and waves. The force of the water contact would rip the engines off very quickly. The extended flaps/flaperons would be next to touch the water. The trailing edges of the flaps/flaperons would start to touch the tops of the swells and waves, and then the entire flap system would be dragged through the water. This is the scenario that led to the erosion on the trailing edge of the flaperon.

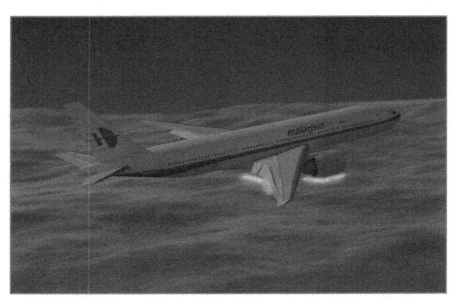

FIGURE 8 A Depiction of MH370 Entering the Water in a Pilot-Controlled Ditching

Imagine the force of the water being directed down and around the trailing edges of the extended (down) flaps/flaperons as the airplane first skimmed the swells and waves, and then descended further into the water. The erosive force of the water would be massive.

As we will see later, there is comparable trailing edge damage on the section of the flap that was recovered from MH370. This was a section of the right outboard flap, the section that had been immediately adjacent to the recovered flaperon. It is not at all surprising to see this similar trailing edge damage on these two adjacent pieces, because the cause for the damage was the same.

This is very important evidence to support the contention that the flaps were extended (down) when the airplane entered the water. From an investigation perspective, it is very fortunate that these two pieces were recovered.

Examination of the Recovered Flap Section

Figure 9 shows the recovered section of wing flap from the right outboard flap (the piece referenced earlier in the discussion about the flaperon).

As you can see, when installed on the airplane this section of recovered flap had been immediately outboard of, and adjacent to, the recovered flaperon.

This section (piece) of flap broke free from the right outboard wing flap. It is the inboard section of the outboard flap. It measures about 15 feet by 6 feet (4.57 meters by 1.83 meters).

From a wreckage perspective, its overall condition is quite similar to the flaperon (basically pristine). It has retained its full aerodynamic shape, with no impact damage to its leading edge, or to its upper and lower surfaces.

We have already calculated that in the scenario put forth by the official investigation, the entire length of MH370 would have been destroyed in about 1/3 second. Similar to the flaperon, this section of flap could not survive in this condition if it had been exposed to the forces of a high-speed diving crash. Again, you do not have to be an experienced investigator to make that determination.

Similar to the damage on the recovered flaperon, there is damage to the trailing edge of this recovered section of the flap. Chunks of the trailing edge have been shattered away. This shattering was caused by multiple water impacts on the trailing edge of the extended (down) flap as the airplane settled into the swells and waves.

As depicted in Figure 8, the sequence would start with the trailing edges of the extended (down) flaps/flaperons touching the tops of the swells and waves. Then, as the airplane lowered into the water surface, the entire flap system would be dragged through the water. The water would be directed down and around the trailing edges of the flaps/flaperons, causing massive erosive forces.

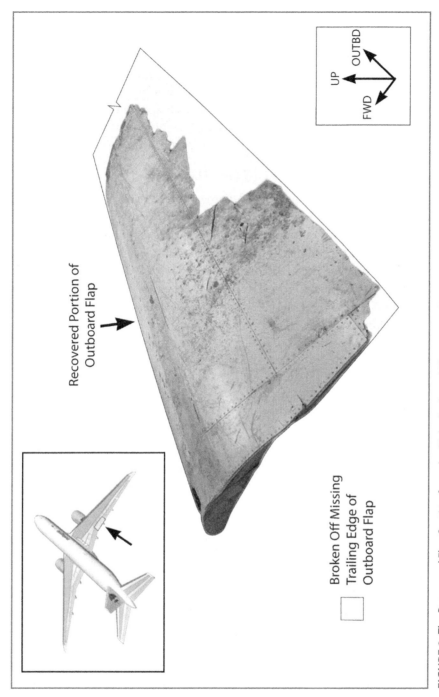

FIGURE 9 The Recovered Flap Section from the Right Outboard Flap – Inset Shows Its Installed Location

35

These massive water forces contributed to the overall force that caused the flaperon and the section of the flap to break free from the airplane. The water forces on these pieces built up as the airplane settled into the water. Eventually, in a short number of seconds, their attachments failed. When they broke free from the wing, they were left behind in the water as the airplane continued to move forward. By being left behind (essentially pulled aft/rearward), they never made contact with the airplane structure ahead of them. This is how their aerodynamic structure (leading edge – top and bottom surfaces) remained pristine.

Aerodynamic Flutter – It Did Not Happen

Among supporters of the high-speed diving crash scenario, the most common explanation for the trailing edge damage to the flaperon and flap section is a phenomenon known as "flutter". Flutter is a severe and destructive vibration caused by dynamic instability. It can occur, for example, when an airplane goes beyond its normal airspeed limit.

There is overwhelming physical evidence to prove that flutter did not happen to MH370. Nevertheless, that is what some people believe happened. The flutter scenario (sequence of events) that they believe happened is as follows:

After the airplane ran out of fuel, it went out of control and entered a spiral dive. The resulting overspeed caused the flutter (severe vibration), and the severe vibration is what damaged the trailing edges on the recovered pieces. Then, the same vibration caused the flaperon and flap section to detach (shake themselves loose) from the wing. Once detached from the airplane, they fell as free bodies into the water.

Flutter supporters (and unpiloted airplane supporters) believe this explains why the recovered pieces are in such an undamaged (pristine) condition. It is because they fell off the airplane while it was still in the air, and never went through the trauma of the high-speed diving crash.

As stated earlier, the evidence shows that there was no flutter. I will explain the basics of flutter, in the context of how it might potentially relate to the MH370 control surfaces.

There are natural vibrations in the control surfaces of all airplanes, and they must be taken into account when the airplane is designed. If the airplane is flown within the limits it was designed for, then the natural vibrations are no problem, and flutter does not happen.

In a high-speed spiral dive, an airplane will surpass its maximum speed. The extreme forces then introduce extra vibrations, over and above the natural vibrations. Flutter in a control surface (such as a flap or flaperon) happens when the frequency of the introduced vibration "couples" with the natural frequency mode vibration already existing in the control surface. In a high-speed spiral dive, all control surfaces on the airplane would be equally susceptible to flutter.

If the frequencies of these two vibrations get in sync, that is, if they couple, the forces multiply. This sets up a violent flutter (unstable oscillations/vibrations) that typically leads to the destruction of the piece (the piece shakes with ever increasing violence until it destroys itself). A severe flutter event can lead to an in-flight breakup of the entire airplane structure.

To detect whether control surface flutter has occurred, investigators can look for significant and distinct physical signatures. For example, with flutter there will be signs of repetitive pounding on the attachments that hold the piece to the airplane. Each individual vibration will potentially leave a pounding mark at the attachment, and there can be a countless number of vibrations. In MH370, there is no such damage.

With control surface flutter, you might also see repetitive pounding between adjacent surfaces. In the case of MH370, there are three places to look for such damage on the recovered pieces: at each end (the outboard end, and the inboard end) of the recovered flaperon, and the inboard end of the outboard flap (the end that was adjacent to the flaperon). You would look for evidence that these ends came together in repetitive contact (evidence that they repeatedly pounded together during their violent oscillations). We can see that there is no such damage on either the recovered flaperon, or the outboard flap section.

As will be explained later, what we do see at these locations on the flaperon and flap section is crushing damage (not repetitive pounding contact) from a single crushing event. They were crushed together during the pilot-controlled ditching. There is absolutely no sign of the kind of repetitive pounding damage that would have resulted from a flutter event.

Had there been flutter, there would also be definitive witness marks on the upper and lower skin surfaces of the recovered pieces. The excessive cyclic twisting forces created by the oscillations will leave these witness marks. With flutter, there will be diagonal cracking in the skin surface. At the very least, there will be diagonal cracking patterns in the painted surfaces. On the recovered pieces, there is no such cracking. These recovered pieces have not been subjected to the kind of twisting and bending that would have occurred with flutter.

Supporters of the flutter theory suggest that the recovered pieces fell as free bodies into the water. Experimentation informs us that when such pieces experience water impact, distinctive witness marks are produced. The next section describes what these witness marks typically look like.

The maximum speed of a free falling object is determined by opposing forces. Gravity pulls the object down, and aerodynamic drag resists. The object reaches its maximum speed, or "terminal velocity", when these two forces are equal.

Through experimentation, we know that the terminal velocity for the flaperon and outboard flap section in free-fall would be around 100 mph (161 kph).

The same experimentation tells us that water impact at that speed generates substantial impact forces, and leaves distinctive witness marks.

Aerodynamically shaped pieces (such as MH370's flaperon and outboard flap section) tend to not tumble as they free-fall. As would be expected, their aerodynamic leading edge tries to lead. Typically, as the piece is falling leading edge first, one corner of the leading edge is lower than the other.

When the piece hits the water surface at this angle, it creates very distinctive witness marks along the leading edge, and at the lead corner. The aerodynamic leading edge is typically pushed in, and has the appearance of being flattened. The corner absorbing the most impact is typically crushed back. We see no such damage on the MH370 pieces.

If the piece happens to land closer to flat on the water surface, the striking skin surface is exposed to distributed hydrodynamic loading that pushes/crushes the skin inward. You can feel this same distributed force if you dive into the water and hit flat (commonly called a belly flop). The interior stiffeners (similar to your ribs in a belly flop) resist this inward force.

In a composite material piece, such as the recovered MH370 pieces, the stressed/compressed skin tends to rebound back to its original shape. However, there will be a definitive geometric cracking pattern left on the impacted surface. This damage pattern would be readily apparent. We see no such damage on the MH370 pieces.

As indicated above, some people suggest that the erosion and shredding at the trailing edges of the flaperon and outboard flap section were caused by vibration during a flutter event. There is no support for this theory. Flutter damage cannot be so isolated that it appears only on the trailing edge.

Even if flutter could produce such damage at the trailing edges, which it could not, there would have to be such significant flutter in the entire piece that other flutter damage, as described above, would be more than evident. There is no doubt that the trailing edge damage that we see on the recovered pieces was caused by hydrodynamic erosion during a flaps-extended, pilot-controlled ditching.

The flutter discussions above show that all the evidence we actually see on the recovered pieces can be used to reject the flutter theory. Upcoming, you will see even more evidence to dismiss the possibility of flutter. You will see evidence that the recovered pieces were still attached normally to the airplane when it entered the water. This additional evidence offers even more proof that these pieces were not torn off the airplane during an airborne flutter event.

Witness Marks Showing Full Flap Extension

This section contains the witness mark evidence showing that MH370's flaps were still attached to the airplane, and fully extended (down), during a pilot-controlled ditching. As has been stated previously, the evidence of flap extension proves that a pilot was controlling the airplane at the end of its flight, and the evidence of a controlled ditching is proof of an intentional act.

We will start with some very basic witness mark investigation. To look for witness mark evidence related to flap position, we can look for any marks made by forced contact between the recovered flaperon, and the recovered (adjacent) section of the flap.

Fortunately, the recovered pieces of wreckage are ideal for finding and examining these types of witness marks. We have the entire flaperon from the right wing, and we have the section of the outboard flap that was immediately adjacent to it.

Figure 10 shows the built-in gaps on both the inboard and outboard ends of the flaperon. These gaps are there so that the flaperon does not make contact with either of the adjacent flaps during normal operation. On the two recovered pieces, this provides us with three locations to look for potential impact-related contact: on the inboard and outboard ends of the flaperon, and on the inboard end of the flap section. Witness marks on these ends can be used to confirm whether the flaps were up (retracted) or down (extended) when the airplane entered the water.

Figure 11 shows a photo where we are looking directly at the inboard end of the outboard flap (in this photo, the flap section is upside down). Specifically, we are looking directly at what is called the end plate, which closes in the inboard end of the flap. The hollow cavity on the opposite side of this endplate is called a seal pan, so technically the end plate closes in the seal pan – you will become familiar with these terms. On the airplane, this end plate would have been immediately adjacent to the flaperon (see Figure 10).

Although it is not apparent from the viewing angle in Figure 11, there is significant crushing damage on this endplate (this endplate is crushed inward – into the seal pan). You will clearly see the crushing in some close up photos below. The crushing damage occurred because this endplate, and the (adjacent) outboard end of the flaperon, were crushed together as the airplane entered the water.

There is a particularly significant witness mark near the aft end of this endplate. Crushing contact with the outboard end of the flaperon created the "V-shaped" black smudge witness mark that is evident (see Figure 11 – the arrow points to the black smudge marking, which looks like a horizontal "V shape"). The significance of this black smudging will be covered in much more detail in the next section.

Also annotated in Figure 11 are two cracks in the endplate that were caused by the crushing forces (see annotations in Figure 11 – "Small Crack" and "Large Crack").

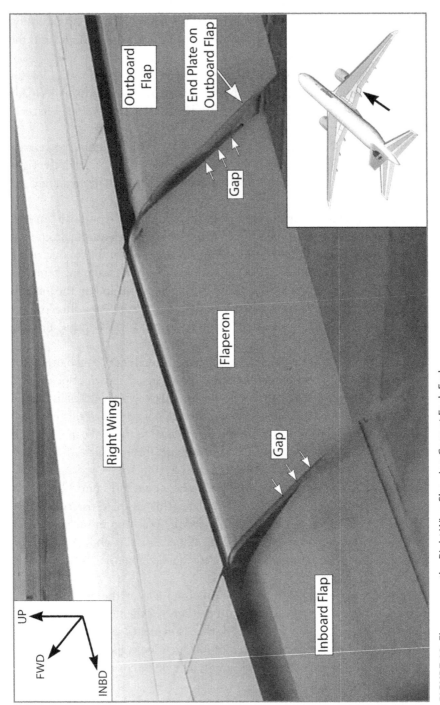

FIGURE 10 Flaperon on the Right Wing Showing Gaps at Each End

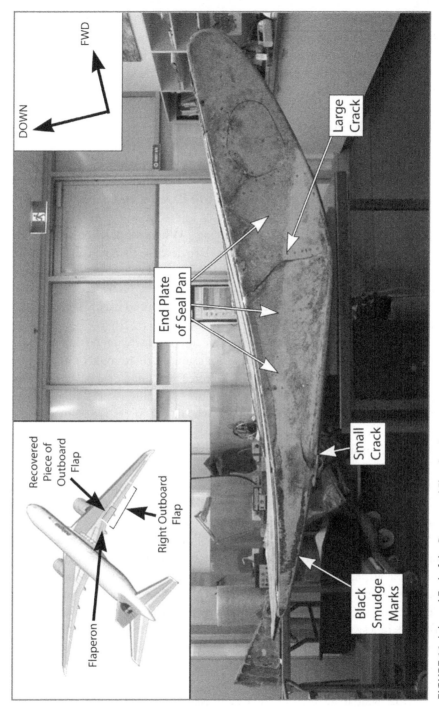

FIGURE 11 Inboard End of the Recovered Flap Section

41

Figure 12 shows a portion of the seal pan side of the end plate. Specifically, it focuses on a close-up view of the smaller crack, from the opposite side.

You can see that the material has been crushed in by the force of the contact with the aft end of the flaperon. The cracking you see was not caused by a puncture; nothing forced its way through. This crack is actually a compression fracture. Such compression fractures occur when the crushing force is so powerful that the material cannot withstand the pressure.

Later, we will examine many more witness marks. Each of the witness marks reveals important evidence about the status of the flaps when MH370 entered the water. But first, it is important to understand what generated the forces that caused these pieces of the flap system (the flaperon, and the outboard flap) to be crushed together.

Here is some basic and useful terminology. When we describe an airplane wing, we talk about its "span", and its "chord". To describe the forces in a crash, we use the terms "spanwise force" and "chordwise force". The direction of a spanwise force is lateral/across – i.e., from a wingtip towards the fuselage, or vice versa. The direction of a chordwise force is longitudinal/front to back – i.e., from the wing's leading edge to its trailing edge.

The terms "spanwise" and "chordwise" are also used when referring to forces generated on other parts of an airplane. For example, there could be a spanwise force generated on the tail, or a chordwise force generated on a passenger seat. Only chordwise forces can be created in a nose first, high-speed diving crash into the water. In a high-speed diving crash, all the forces are from forward to aft (chordwise).

Figure 13 provides a visual depiction of these forces.

This evidence of crushing between the flaperon and outboard flap confirms that when MH370 entered the water, there was a spanwise force generated along the trailing edge of the right wing. Later, we will examine other evidence that confirms the presence of this spanwise force.

So the question is, how was this spanwise force generated? I will give you the answer now, because it will allow you to better follow the information below. When the airplane entered the water, it was in a wings-level attitude, as depicted in Figure 8. At some point, as the airplane slowed down upon touching the water surface, the right wing dipped down until the wingtip struck the top of a wave or a swell. The right wingtip then dug into the water. This is how the spanwise force was generated along the trailing edge of the right wing – from the force of the right wingtip being held back. Again, all this happened during a pilot-controlled ditching.

The following investigation experiment clearly demonstrates how this spanwise force was created. To see it for yourself, you will need a paper cutout of the basic shape of a B777, looking down from directly overhead. You can use

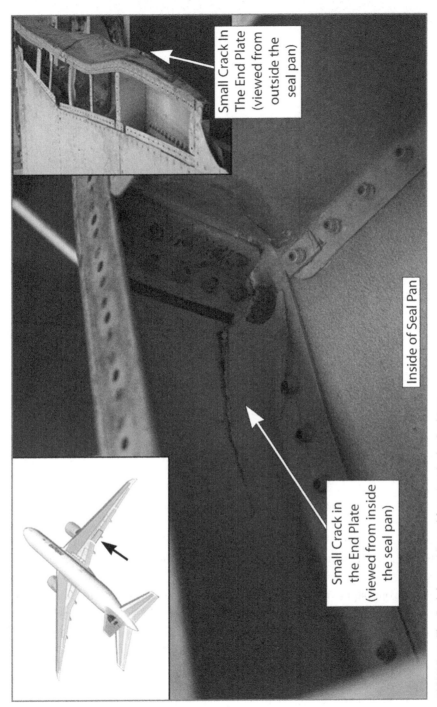

Small Crack In The End Plate (viewed from outside the seal pan)

Inside of Seal Pan

Small Crack in the End Plate (viewed from inside the seal pan)

FIGURE 12 The Endplate as Viewed from Inside the Seal Pan

43

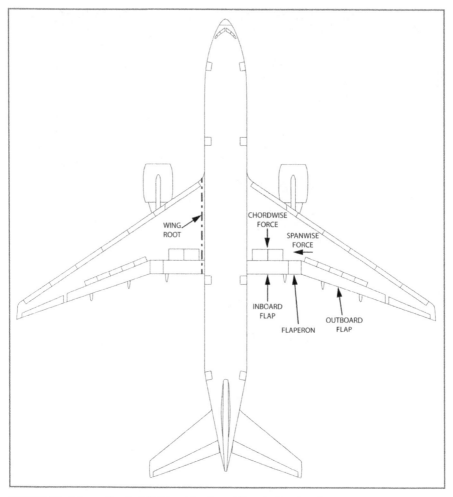

FIGURE 13 Schematic of a B777 Looking from Directly Overhead

the Figure 13 diagram as a guide, or download and print the shape from the internet. This experiment does not require a complicated or exact shape; a basic airplane shape works very well.

Place your paper airplane shape on a firm and flat surface. While holding the fuselage and left wing in place, gently move the right wingtip rearward. This simulates the right wingtip being held back by the force of the water. When you move the right wingtip rearward, you will see the trailing edge of the right wing being lifted (rising upwards) away from the flat surface.

What you have created is a spanwise force along the wing's trailing edge. This is the exact same spanwise force that was created along the trailing edge of MH370's right wing when the right wingtip dug into the water. This is the same spanwise force that caused the flaperon and outboard flap to compress together.

Unlike a paper wing, the actual wing structure on the airplane will resist this upward bending. To simulate the structural strength in the actual wing, gently hold the paper wing down (do not let it lift up) as you move the wingtip rearward. You will see that instead of folding upwards at only one place, the spanwise force now causes the trailing edge to fold upwards and downwards in a wave pattern. This wave pattern better represents what actually happened to MH370's wing when the spanwise force was generated.

It is important to understand that this spanwise force along the wing's trailing edge cannot be created unless the wing root (see "Wing Root" in Figure 1 and Figure 13) is firmly attached to the fuselage. On your paper airplane, you can remove the holding force at the wing root by simply cutting the wing free from the fuselage. With the wing cut off, move the wingtip rearward and it becomes very obvious that removing the resistance (the anchor point at the fuselage) makes it impossible to create any spanwise force along the wing's trailing edge.

This tells us that when MH370's right wingtip entered the water, the fuselage of the airplane still had full structural integrity. If the fuselage were not fully intact, the wing would have nothing to be attached to. We know that if there had been a high-speed diving crash, the structural integrity of the fuselage would have been lost in the blink of an eye because of the hydrodynamic forces disintegrating the fuselage from front to back. Again, in a high-speed diving crash there would be no solid fuselage for the wing root to stay attached to, and therefore it would not have been possible to generate the spanwise force that the evidence clearly shows.

All this evidence provides further proof that MH370 did not enter the water in a high-speed diving crash.

Examination of the "V-Shaped" Black Smudge Witness Marks

We will now look further at the "V-shaped" black smudge witness marks that are evident on the endplate of the recovered outboard flap section. We saw these smudge marks earlier, in Figure 11. A different view can be seen in Figure 14.

In the Figure 14 photo, the flap section is positioned upside down. We can see that the investigators have removed an access panel to allow a view inside the seal pan.

Later we will examine witness marks inside the seal pan, but for now we will concentrate on the "V-shaped" black smudge witness marking on the outside of the endplate. The black smudging was created by severe crushing between the outboard end of the flaperon, and this endplate. The flaperon and flap were crushed together by the spanwise force acting along the trailing edge of the wing.

Figure 15 shows the two parts that were crushed together, with the arrows pointing to examples of the mating surfaces – specifically to the mating surfaces that created the black smudging.

45

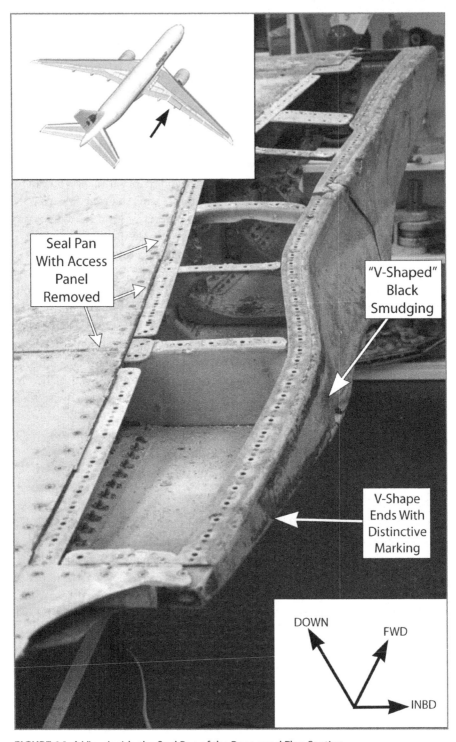

Seal Pan
With Access
Panel
Removed

"V-Shaped"
Black
Smudging

V-Shape
Ends With
Distinctive
Marking

DOWN
FWD
INBD

FIGURE 14 A View Inside the Seal Pan of the Recovered Flap Section

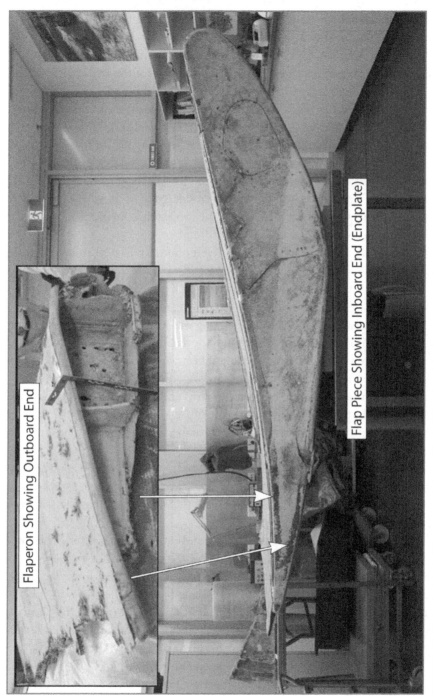

Flaperon Showing Outboard End

Flap Piece Showing Inboard End (Endplate)

FIGURE 15 Outboard End of Flaperon – Inboard End of Flap Section

47

The spanwise force caused the outboard end of the flaperon to crush into the inboard end of the outboard flap (see Figure 15). Note that some of the outermost structure at the bottom/rear of the flaperon is gone. That is the part that actually caused some of the black smudging, and the material broke off when the crushing contact happened.

We can examine this black smudging even more closely, and extract additional evidence. Figure 16 is used for reference in the explanations that follow.

In the top left photo in Figure 16, we can see that the outboard edges of the flaperon are covered with aerodynamic strips, which we will call rub strips. There is one on the bottom, and one on the top. Their purpose is to help fill the gap space between the flaperon and the flap, for improved aerodynamic airflow. You can see that the rub strip on the top extends further rearward than the one on the bottom.

In the top right photo, and the bottom left photo (in Figure 16), you can see that the "V shape" black smudge marking ends with distinctive marking (also see Figure 14). There is a near straight line, but you can also see that there is a narrow trail of further smudge marking going aft.

We can clearly see that the black smudging was made by the flaperon's top and bottom rub strips as they were crushed into the flap. The actual transfer of material can be attributed to a significant amount of heat being generated at that location because of the friction as the pieces rubbed together under extreme pressure.

At the location where the bottom rub strip ends, the black smudging indicates that the bottom rub strip was moving up against the top rub strip, leaving the straight line marking. The aft trail of further smudging was deposited by the extended piece of the top rub strip.

These witness marks reveal much about what was happening when the flaperon and flap crushed together from the spanwise loading. Most significantly, they tell us the relative position between the flap and flaperon as the spanwise loading was crushing them together.

The bottom right photo in Figure 16 can be used for reference. The force of the spanwise loading caused the flaperon to crush into the outboard flap. The first crushing contact happened towards the flaperon's leading edge. There is a natural pivot point where the gap widens between the flaperon and the flap, where the arrow points to the "large crack" in the bottom right photo in Figure 16. If you refer back to Figure 11, you can see the large crack that resulted from the compression stress at this pivot point.

The flaperon pivoted around this pressure point. The crushing along the trailing edge of the wing was causing the flaperon to pivot and slide in an aft direction as it was making contact with the outboard flap. The location of all this black smudging, and the other crushing witness marks in the endplate, reveal the positional relationship between the flap and the flaperon at the time the crushing was

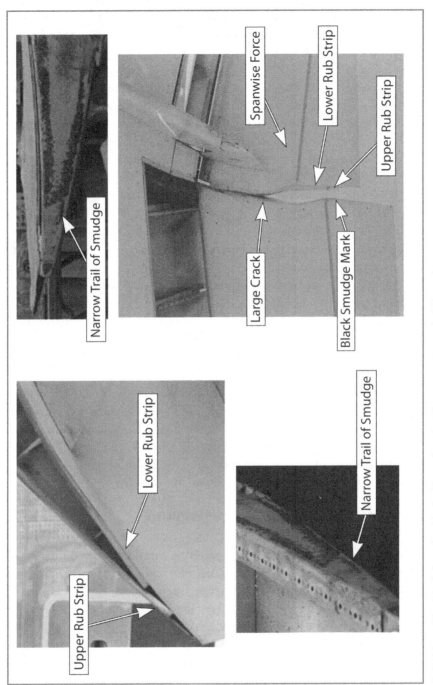

FIGURE 16 The Black Smudge Marks Show that the Flaps Were Extended (Down)

49

taking place. The alignments fit with a flaps-extended architecture, and not with a flaps-retracted architecture. The locations of the witness marks prove that the flaps were fully extended when the spanwise crushing took place. The spanwise crushing happened as the airplane was entering the water.

Only a controlled ditching scenario fits with the witness mark evidence. More details regarding the controlled ditching sequence will come later, but to put context to the above evidence, the basic sequence is outlined below.

With the engines still running, and the airplane still fully serviceable, the pilot descended to the ocean surface to intentionally conduct a controlled ditching. Nearing the end of his descent, he selected the flaps to full down. He left the landing gear retracted (up); this would be standard for a controlled ditching. The airplane approached the ocean surface at about 140 knots (161 mph, 259 kph), and then slowed as the pilot raised the nose to transition to a landing (controlled ditching) attitude. The aircraft then descended slowly to the water surface (see Figure 8).

The engines made the first contact, and they were ripped off. Then, the trailing edges of the flaps and flaperons started to make contact with the tops of the waves and swells. This is what caused the damage we see on their trailing edges. At some point, the right wing dipped (see further discussion later), and the right wingtip dug into the crest of a wave/swell. This created the spanwise force along the trailing edge of the right wing.

As the flaperon and flaps penetrated deeper into the water, the water force against them increased. It was the combination of this water force, and the spanwise force along the trailing edge of the wing, that caused their attachments to let go, allowing them to be left behind. By being left behind, they did not make any contact with the wing structure ahead of them. This is how they emerged as we see them, in basically pristine condition.

Further Assessment of the Flap/Flaperon Position At Water Entry

A critical part of any accident investigation is the detailed examination of wreckage pieces. Experienced investigators, who have expertise in finding and interpreting witness marks, lead this work. They analyze every scratch and dent and twist and puncture and smudge. They try to determine the impact related forces, and to piece together the breakup sequence of the airplane. This critical activity forms part of every thorough and proper investigation. This critical activity was either not done, or not done correctly, during the MH370 investigation.

The ATSB first released the official investigation's take on flap position in a document titled, *MH370 – Search and debris examination update*, dated 2 November 2016. Follow-up comments are included in their Final Report, titled, *The Operational Search for MH370*, dated 3 October 2017. Both of these documents are available on their website.

Regarding information about their examination of the flaperon and flap section, and their conclusion about flap position, these two documents basically say the same thing. They incorrectly conclude that the flaps were retracted at impact. I will comment specifically on the ATSB's 2 November 2016 update document. It was released during the official investigation's active search for the wreckage of MH370, and therefore was most influential in how that search was being conducted.

The main focus of this 2 November 2016 ATSB update document was on the process being used to define the grid boundaries for their underwater wreckage search. They started with an updated analysis of the satellite communications used to track MH370 to the southern Indian Ocean.

Their interpretation of this satellite communication led them to believe that the airplane ran out of fuel, and that it entered a high-speed dive with an ever-increasing rate of descent. We know that neither of these events actually happened.

Their update document included information about performance testing completed in a B777 simulator, where they simulated the B777 running out of fuel. Not surprisingly, the simulator testing confirmed the likelihood that if a B777 ran out of fuel it would enter a high-speed dive, with an ever-increasing rate of descent. Using the simulator, they also established parameters for how far the airplane could travel without engine power. They used that information to help define the search grid boundaries.

The 2 November 2016 ATSB update document then provided new information on the wreckage drift modelling that was undertaken to locate the starting place for the drifting (i.e., the crash site).

Then, at the end of this update document, the ATSB released their assessment of the recovered flaperon, and the recovered section of the outboard flap. Their analysis (incorrectly) led them to believe that MH370's flaps were fully up when the airplane struck the water.

The wreckage analysis used by the ATSB to support their finding about flap position is unworthy of a professional investigation. Not only did the ATSB selectively choose the most supportive witness marks to analyze, they completely misinterpreted the witness marks they did analyze. This substandard wreckage analysis is central to what went wrong with the overall MH370 investigation. I will expand on this later, but for context here, I offer the following.

The ATSB needed a "flaps up" finding in their 2 November 2016 update document to support their theory of a high-speed dive, followed by a high-speed crash. Without a "flaps up" finding, the entire MH370 investigation, and their search for wreckage, would be turned on its head.

An opposite finding of "flaps down" would invalidate their theory of an un-piloted airplane, because that would mean the airplane did not run out of fuel. Without a fuel exhaustion starting point, there would be no way to reasonably calculate a search grid to look for wreckage. In other words, a "flaps down" finding would have completely invalidated the calculations they had already used to determine their wreckage search grid.

We will now examine the evidence used in the ATSB's 2 November 2016 update document to support their incorrect finding of "flaps up". Specific to the flaperon, their analysis is very limited; it offers only the following, under the title "Flap position", on Page 21:

> With the flap in the retracted position, alignment of the flap and flaperon rear spar lines, along with the close proximity of the two parts, indicated a probable relationship between the two areas of damage around the rear spars of the parts. This was consistent with contact between the two parts during the aircraft breakup sequence, indicating that the flaperon was probably aligned with the flap, at or close to the neutral (faired) position.

The ATSB update document analysis ends with the following, on Page 26:

> The right flaperon was probably at, or close to, the neutral position at the time it separated from the wing.

The ATSB made no attempt to explain the overall pristine condition of the flaperon. They gave no explanation for how, in a high-speed diving crash, the flaperon could retain its aerodynamic shape, or its undamaged leading edge. There was nothing about the lack of damage to its upper and lower surfaces.

They did acknowledge there had been contact between the flaperon and the outboard flap, but they made no attempt to explain what forces produced that contact. They did not explain that the crushing could only have been from a spanwise force along the wing's trailing edge. They appeared unaware that such a spanwise force could not be created during a high-speed diving impact, an impact into the water that would start and finish in the blink of an eye.

They referred to "contact between the two parts during the aircraft breakup sequence". They did not recognize that in a high-speed diving crash, there is no classic breakup sequence. The entire wing entry into the water would take about 4/100 of a second. Hydrodynamic forces from the water invasion would explosively rupture the wings, and the flaps, and the flaperons, all from the inside out. There would be no time to create a spanwise force to cause the parts to crush together.

The fact is that there was no high-speed diving crash. The extended flaperon was simply torn free by a combination of the build-up of water forces as it was pulled through the water, and the spanwise forces along the trailing edge of the wing. When these combined forces exceeded the strength of the attachments, the flaperon broke free from the back of the wing, and it was left behind in the water.

We will now turn to the recovered piece from the right outboard flap. In the ATSB's 2 November 2016 update document, their analysis of that piece is both inaccurate and exceptionally incomplete. Of the many witness marks available, they chose to reference only those they thought supported their finding of "flaps up". Then, they misinterpreted the witness marks they chose.

The analysis of the outboard flap section is more complex than for the flaperon. The flaperon is easier to analyze because it simply broke free from the back of the wing as one piece, when its attachments let go. The recovered flap section is more complex because it had first broken from the rest of the flap, and then it detached from the back of the wing.

Fortunately, there are witness marks that reveal the sequence of events that led to the flap section being liberated from the airplane. The ATSB update document made no attempt to explain how this happened. The analysis below explains it in detail.

Figure 17 shows how the outboard flap is attached to the wing.

The outboard flap is held to the wing at two very robust attachment points (see annotation). The hydraulic actuators (long hydraulic cylinders) that extend and retract the flap are also located at these two attachments. The pods that cover the hydraulic cylinders are commonly referred to as "canoes", and they are there to provide aerodynamic streamlining.

Also annotated in Figure 17 is the location of the seal pan, which we are already familiar with (see Figure 14) at the inboard end of the flap. The seal pan provides a cavity for another attachment point for the flap. This innermost attachment is much less robust than the two main attachments, because it is designed only to provide stability at the inner end of the flap. It plays no role in hydraulically moving the flap up or down.

An integral (and biggest) piece of the inboard end attachment (at the seal pan) is a long, slightly curved, chordwise arm called a support track (see Figure 18).

The front of the support track is very solidly attached to the back of the wing. From this attachment point, the support track sticks out chordwise (rearward) into the seal pan through a hole designed for that purpose. When the flaps are fully retracted (up), the support track is inserted all the way inside the seal pan. When the flaps are extended (down), only the very back end of the support track is still inserted into the seal pan.

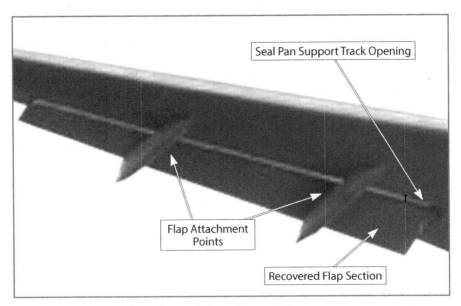

Seal Pan Support Track Opening

Flap Attachment Points

Recovered Flap Section

FIGURE 17 Depiction of Attachment Points – Flaps to Wing

For clarity, when the flaps are fully retracted (up), the entire length of the support track is inside the seal pan. When the flaps are fully extended (down), almost the entire length of the support track is outside the seal pan, with only the aft end of it still remaining inside. The sole purpose of the support track is to serve as a solid (non-moving) piece of structure (firmly attached to the back of the wing).

There is a carriage assembly attached to the support track, and that carriage assembly is also attached to the flap (it is attached just inside the front end of the seal pan). The way it works is that when the flaps are going down and up (extending and retracting), the carriage assembly runs back and forth along the support track, and because it is attached to both the support track and the flap, it provides extra stability to that end of the flap.

With that description, it is easy to see why any investigator would be anxious to look for witness marks inside the seal pan of the recovered flap section. Any marks made by contact/impact between the support track and the inside of the seal pan could be used to determine how far the support track was inserted into the seal pan when the airplane entered the water. If you could determine that, then you could establish with a high degree of certainty whether the flaps were retracted (up), or extended (down).

Neither the support track nor the carriage assembly were recovered. Thankfully, and critically, the seal pan was recovered (as we have seen, it is part of the recovered outboard flap section).

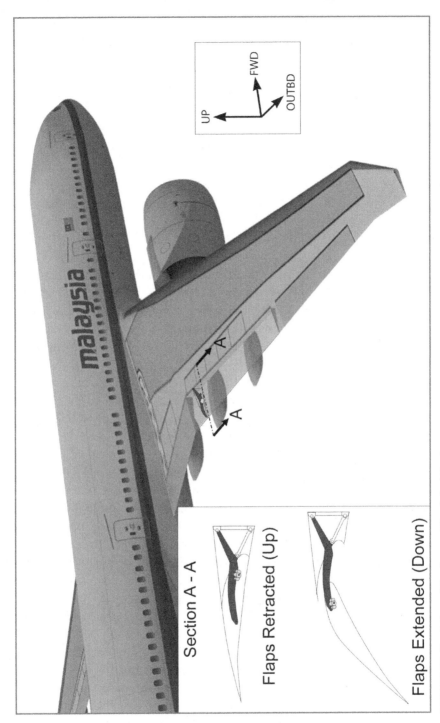

FIGURE 18 Depiction of the Support Track Architecture

Based on their inspection and analysis of the seal pan, here is what the ATSB update document had to say about flap position – this information is extracted from their 2 November 2016 update document.

The ATSB's observations, on Page 21:

> Two adjacent aluminum stiffeners within the inboard seal pan area exhibited impact damage. The damage was significant because it was indicative of impact damage and the only component in the vicinity of the stiffeners, capable of independent movement within the seal pan, was the support track. Measurements of the support track position at various stages of flap deployment, indicated that the track would have to be fully inserted into the flap in the retracted position to be adjacent to the damaged stiffeners.

The ATSB is correct in saying that the damage on the two adjacent aluminum stiffeners inside the seal pan could only come from impact with the support track. They are also correct in saying that the support track had to have been inside the seal pan when that impact happened. The remainder of the ATSB's analysis of the seal pan is not correct. It is both simplistic, and incomplete.

The ATSB's interpretation is that these witness marks inside the seal pan were created when the airplane struck the water at high speed. They assume that the witness marks represent the relative position of the support track to the aluminum stiffeners at the time of impact. By making that (incorrect) assumption, they were able to conclude that the damage inside the seal pan provides proof that the flaps were retracted (up) at the moment of impact (which of course means that the flaps were retracted (up) prior to impact).

There is proof, as you will see, that the witness marks inside the seal pan confirm the exact opposite of the ATSB's analysis. The witness marks reveal that the flaps were in a fully extended (down) position when the airplane entered the water, and that the recovered flap section had undergone some violent movements, during a pilot-controlled ditching, before it was finally released (it broke free) from the trailing edge of the wing.

What we will see is that when this recovered piece broke free from the rest of the flap, its inboard end was thrust violently to a fully up position. In fact, this flap section actually retracted to beyond a fully up position, prior to when it was released from the wing and left behind in the water.

I do not expect that you will be able to visualize these violent flap movements right now, but as we go through the evidence you will see that there is proof of what actually happened, and the evidence is very clear, and it is not difficult to follow.

We can look first at some evidence that is very easy to understand. Figure 19 shows the recovered section of the outboard flap.

This view is of the top surface of the recovered outboard flap section, looking from the inboard end. We can see the leading edge, and the end plate on the seal pan. The hole that we can see at the inboard front corner is where the support track enters into the seal pan. The carriage assembly that travels along the support track attaches to the flap just inside this hole. The support track and carriage assembly were not recovered, so we do not have those to examine.

But we still have all the evidence we need. We know that the carriage assembly is attached to the flap just inside the hole. We know that when the flaps are fully up (retracted), the entire length of the support track is inside the seal pan, and when the flaps are fully down (extended), most of the support track is outside the seal pan. However, at all times at least the aft end of the support track is still inside the seal pan where the carriage assembly is attached to it.

When the flap section broke free, the support track (with the carriage assembly still attached to it) had to have exited out of the seal pan. A curious investigator would ask: what was their exit point out of the seal pan? Another question; what crash dynamic forces were involved in separating the flap from the carriage assembly (which is attached to the flap inside the seal pan)?

These are very basic investigation questions. It is puzzling that they were not addressed by the official investigation. It seems they did not do any analysis of this. We will do our own analysis.

In Figure 20, we can observe damage around the edges of the entry hole into the seal pan.

There are no other holes in the seal pan where the support track with the attached carriage assembly could have exited. Therefore, we can conclude that the support track, with the attached carriage assembly, pulled out through that damaged hole in the front of the seal pan. That pulling out is what caused the damage around the hole.

Now, we can assess what relative movements of the wing and the flap (relative to each other) would allow the support track and carriage assembly to pull out through that hole. The only answer is that relative to each other, the wing had to be going forward, and the flap had to be going (relatively) aft.

The airplane was moving forward, so to create the relative aft movement of the flap, the flap must have been being held back. In other words, the flap had to have separated from the wing by being pulled towards the aft. That is the only way the support track and carriage assembly could have been pulled out through that hole.

This analysis, explaining how the relative movement between the wing and the flap section was created, is not difficult. There are no other complicating factors, such as some convoluted explanation involving "crash dynamics". It is

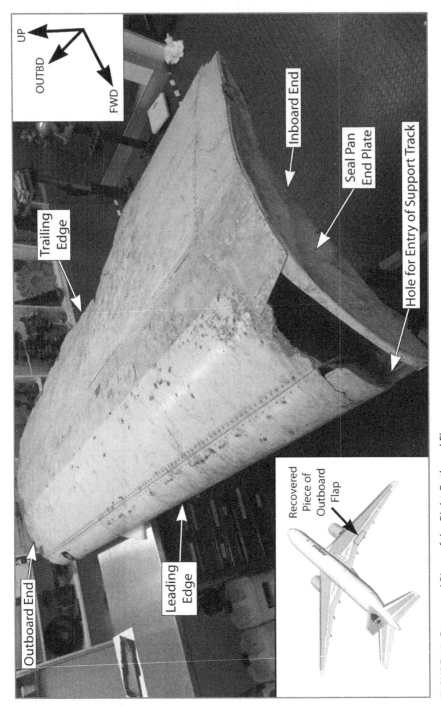

FIGURE 19 Recovered Piece of the Right Outboard Flap

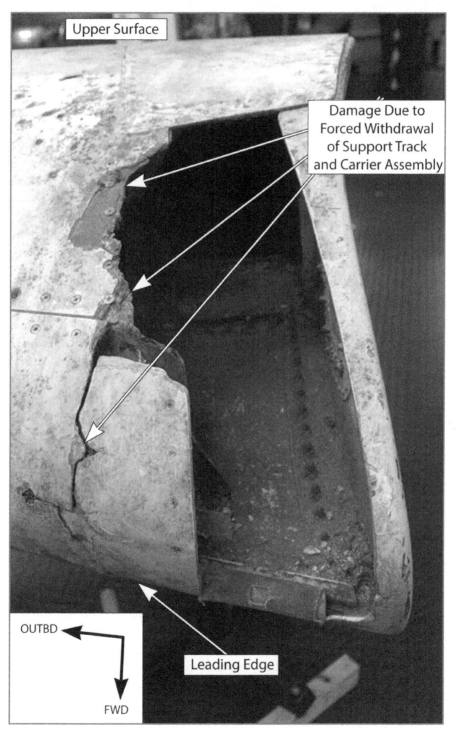

Upper Surface

Damage Due to
Forced Withdrawal
of Support Track
and Carrier Assembly

OUTBD

FWD

Leading Edge

FIGURE 20 Damage at the Entry Hole Into the Seal Pan

as simple as it seems, and is based on easily understandable logic and physics. You do not have to be an experienced investigator to figure it out.

It is also not difficult to figure out where the aft forces on the flap had to have come from. The answer is that when MH370 entered the water, the flaps were extended (down). The aft forces were created because the extended (down) flap was being pulled through the water, and the flap was being held back. There would be no aft force on the flap if it had been fully retracted (up) in a streamlined position.

That explains how the support track and carriage assembly got pulled out through the hole at the front of the seal pan. This is proof that the flaps were extended (down) when the airplane entered the water.

From what has been made available from the official investigation, it appears they made no attempt to analyze any of this. Had they tried, they might have quickly realized that their high-speed diving crash scenario does not fit the evidence; in fact, it makes no sense.

In a high-speed diving crash with the flaps fully retracted (up), how could the fully inserted support track have exited from the seal pan through the hole at the front? How would the aft movement of the flap have been generated? All of the momentum would be forward. They would have to explain how an aft force to pull the full length of the support track out through the hole in the front of the seal pan could be created in 4/100 of a second, while at the same time leaving the leading edge of the flap in pristine condition.

The evidence just presented is by itself sufficient to prove that there was no high-speed diving crash. Simple physics shows that the scenario supported by the ATSB is physically impossible.

The ATSB referred to damage inside the seal pan to conclude the flaps were retracted (up) at water impact. Their analysis is incomplete, and entirely inaccurate. We will do our own analysis.

As I mentioned earlier, the ATSB made one observation with which I am in full agreement. That is their observation that the witness mark damage inside the seal pan could only be caused by contact between the support track and the seal pan.

What the ATSB failed to address in their observations is the full extent of the damage inside the seal pan. The evidence shows there were multiple impacts with the support track. There are witness marks on the top of the seal pan, and on the bottom, and on each side, and on each end.

There could be no contact between the support track, and the inside of the seal pan, unless one of them had broken free of its support structure. Either the support track had broken free and was making contact with the inside of the seal pan, or the flap section (that has the seal pan at its inboard end) had broken free, allowing the seal pan to make contact with the support track.

It is easy to assess which one had broken free. We know that the support track and carriage assembly were pulled out through the hole at the front of the seal pan. Therefore, the support track had to have been still attached to the wing, because if it were not, there would be nothing holding on to it to pull it out. Therefore, we can conclude it was the flap section that had broken free. It was the flap section that was loose and making contact with the support track, and not the other way around.

This is an important observation because of what we see in Figure 21. We are looking inside the seal pan at pieces that are bent; some are bent forward toward the leading edge of the flap section, and some are bent aft toward the trailing edge.

Figure 21 provides various views inside the seal pan.

We see in Figure 21 that there is damage inside the seal pan showing that at one time the flap section was moving from aft to forward, and then at another time was moving from forward to aft. In other words, during the sequence that caused the flap section to break free, it had moved in two different directions – toward retract (up), and toward extend (down).

I would like to assure you that this is not as confusing as it might seem. Actually, as you will see later, it is not difficult to follow. The entire sequence will be explained in the following pages, and you will understand how it happened. To prepare you for the upcoming explanations, here is the sequence of movements of the flap section that produced the witness marks in Figure 21:

1. The starting position for the intact outboard flap was full down – as selected by the pilot for the controlled ditching;

2. After entering the water, the recovered flap section broke free (was liberated) from the rest of the outboard flap, but it was still loosely connected to the wing at the seal pan by the support track and carriage assembly;

3. The force of the water drove the liberated flap section to full retract (up) – this created the witness marks inside the seal pan that confirm forward (towards up/retracted) movement of the flap section;

4. Then, the liberated flap section was pulled aft by the water forces – this pulled the support track and carriage assembly out through the hole in the front of the seal pan – this is what created the witness marks inside the seal pan that confirm aft (towards down/extended) movement of the flap section.

The visual evidence of both forward and aft movement damage is clearly evident in Figure 21. You will see below that the analysis of how that damage

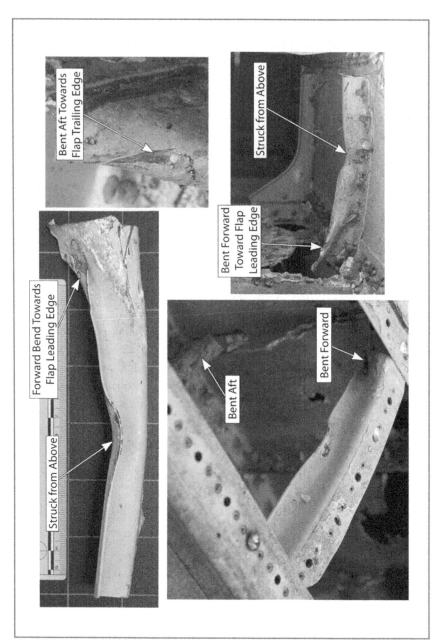

FIGURE 21 Inside the Seal Pan – Damage from Two Different Directions

62

was created is not nearly as complex as you might think – you will be able to understand it. For now, you only need to see that the witness marks in Figure 21 clearly show damage from movement in two entirely different directions – one forward, and one aft.

I will add the following here for context. It would be impossible for this damage inside the seal pan to occur in a flaps-up, high-speed diving crash. There is no logical high-speed crash dynamic that could explain both the forward and aft movement of the flap section. In a high-speed diving crash, the destruction of the wing would be virtually instantaneous (in 4/100 of a second), with only forward momentum. The laws of physics do not allow things to move both forward and aft at the same time.

As I mentioned above, the evidence that reveals how the flap section moved to create both fore and aft damages inside the seal pan is readily available, and relatively easy to understand. We will start the explanation by looking first at the opposite end of the recovered flap section.

Figure 22 below shows the bottom of the recovered flap section, looking along the leading edge from the outboard end.

Figure 22 shows the section of jagged metal from the flap mount that broke off and stayed attached to the outboard end of the recovered flap section. In service, this flap mount would be hidden behind the aerodynamic canoe as shown in Figure 17. This jagged metal is part of the inboard mount that connects the outboard flap to the wing. Specifically, what we see is a piece of what is called the flap track support.

Also highlighted in Figure 22 is the fracture where this recovered flap section severed from the remainder of the right outboard flap. The flap broke in an almost perfect straight line, chordwise, along the seam just outboard of the chordwise stiffener inside the flap – the stiffener that the flap mount is attached to.

For clarity and orientation, this section of the flap that we see, the piece that was recovered, is about one-third of the right outboard flap; in other words, what was recovered is the inboard one-third of the right outboard flap.

A more close-up view of the broken/bent push-pull rod can be seen in Figure 23.

The broken push/pull rod shown (see Figures 22 and 23) is part of the push/pull rod used to extend and retract the flap. The power that pushes and pulls the rod comes from the airplane's hydraulic system. In Figure 23 you can see where the rod is attached to the pivot mechanism that allows it to rotate as the flap extends and retracts.

These flap tracks, and chord-wise stiffeners, and push/pull rods, are tremendously strong. In service, they must not only withstand the forces that move the flap up and down, they must hold on to the flap when it is lowered down into the airflow.

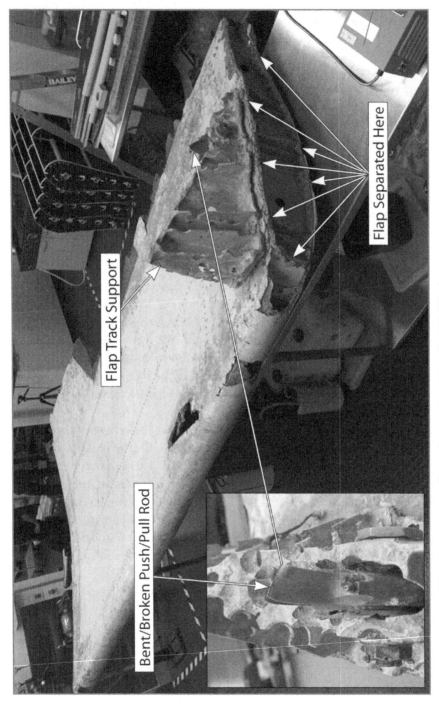

Flap Separated Here

Flap Track Support

Bent/Broken Push/Pull Rod

FIGURE 22 Fractured Flap Mount – Insert Shows Fractured and Bent Push/Pull Rod

64

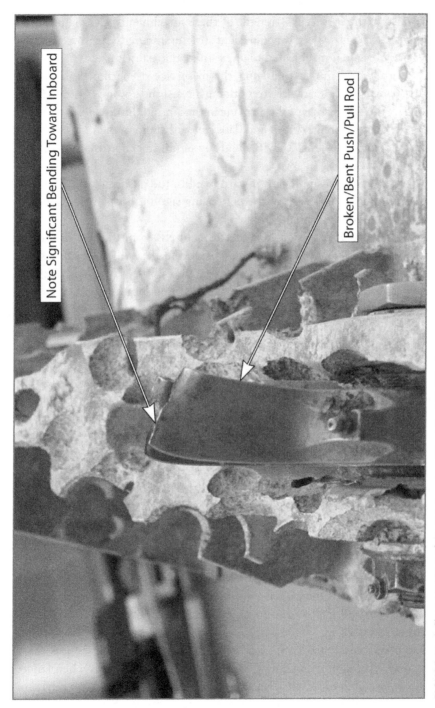

Note Significant Bending Toward Inboard

Broken/Bent Push/Pull Rod

FIGURE 23 A Close Up View of the Fractured and Bent Push/Pull Rod

By design, the in-service strength of these attachment pieces is primarily chordwise. There is no need for equivalent structural strength spanwise, because in service they are not subjected to any significant spanwise loads.

Conversely, and similar to a wing, the in-service strength of a flap is primarily spanwise. The spanwise strength must resist the upward bending forces created by the lift that keeps the airplane in the air, and the downward bending forces of a hard landing. Wings and flaps can withstand tremendous spanwise forces, but are not designed to withstand any significant chordwise forces, such as impact forces.

Figure 23 shows a significant inward bend in the push/pull rod. The bend in this rod informs us that it was experiencing significant spanwise (inboard) bending loads before it finally broke.

The recovered flap section separated (fractured) from the rest of the flap immediately adjacent to the stiffener inside the flap. This informs us that a significant bending (buckling) force was acting all the way across that seam to cause the clean (straight chordwise) break at that location.

In accident investigation, it is standard procedure to analyze all this type of evidence to determine the crash dynamics involved. We need to assess what forces led to the bending and fracturing of the push/pull rod, and what forces caused the clean fracture of the flap at the seam line along the flap stiffener. It is not clear whether any analysis of this was done by the official investigation, but if it was, none of that analysis was released. Therefore, we will do our own analysis here.

From our experiments with the paper airplane, we know that the spanwise force acting along the trailing edge of the right wing was created when the right wingtip dug into the water. We know that this spanwise force would be resisted at the fuselage (at the wing root), and because of this resistance, the trailing edge of the wing would start to buckle. We know that the stiffness of the wing would resist the buckling. We know that this resistance would create a wave pattern in the buckling. There would be some upward buckling, and some downward buckling.

It was this spanwise force, and the resultant buckling, that caused the flap to fracture the way it did at the seam line along the flap stiffener. What is interesting here is that the evidence in Figure 24 actually allows us to conclude that the recovered flap section fractured because of downward buckling, and not upward buckling.

The marks annotated with arrows in Figure 24 are classic witness marks known as "overlapping gouging". This is gouging that happens when failures occur from compressive buckling loads. The gouges were made by dynamic spanwise overlapping movement during the fracturing/separation.

You can use a tissue box to do a quick experiment that shows it was downward buckling that caused the failure, and the overlapping gouging. The tissue box represents a pre-impact and fully intact flap. With one hand at each end of the tissue box, apply a spanwise buckling force that buckles the top of the box down in the middle. (In simple terms, push in on both ends of the box and force the top of the box to buckle downward in the middle.) The top surface of the box is being compressed, and if it were solid material it would break apart at the location of the buckle.

Now apply a force in the opposite direction, by trying to force the box to buckle upwards. You will quickly see that the top of the box will not buckle upwards because the force you are applying is trying to pull it apart. This demonstrates that it could only have been a downward buckle that caused the overlapping gouging on the top surface of the box (flap). The downward compressive buckling loads would push the fractured pieces together (and cause the overlapping gouging), whereas an up buckle would pull the fractured pieces apart at the top, leaving no potential for overlapping.

In your tissue box experiment for downward compressive buckling, the wrinkle across the top of the box represents the line where the eventual fracture will occur. At the end of that wrinkle line (that represents the eventual fracture), you will see a bulge. That bulge represents end-point damage caused by the buckling. You can see the equivalent of that damage, as annotated in Figure 24. What is annotated is very distinctive end-point damage at the corner of the leading edge, caused by the downward buckling.

Again, this type of analysis should not be difficult for seasoned investigators. You can see the witness marks yourself. The end-point damage is a classic

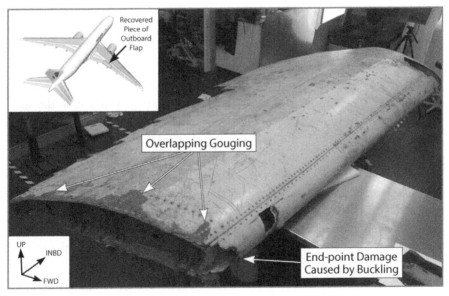

FIGURE 24 Overlapping Gouging from Compressive Buckling Loads

67

indicator of compressive buckling. Supporters of the high-speed diving crash scenario would not be able to explain what force (in their scenario) caused that specific damage, at that specific location, but left the remainder of the leading edge pristine. Once again, any explanation involving a high-speed diving crash would come into conflict with the laws of physics.

I will add a short paragraph here to address those investigators with a keen eye who might see that there is also some relatively minor gouging along the fracture seam on the bottom surface of the flap section. This is initial gouging that happened on both the top and the bottom surfaces. It occurred immediately before, or just as, the actual downward buckling started, and was caused by the initial compressive forces pushing that seam (on both the top and bottom) towards overlap. The major overlapping gouging on the top surface occurred when the downward buckling caused the fracturing seam to override the top surface, as described above.

We will now examine another witness mark that is important to see before we can fully analyze the failure sequence for the recovered flap section. Figure 25 below is looking aft, into the aft end of the seal pan.

As annotated, there is a very distinctive witness mark that was created on that stiffener bracket when the aft blunt end of the support track made contact with it. Here is how we know it was the aft end of the support track that made the witness mark.

First, we know that the support track was the only object inside the seal pan that was capable of making contact with anything. Second, we know that the aft end of the support track was facing towards the aft of the seal pan, so it was aimed in the right direction. And third, by observing the location and shape of the witness mark, we can see that the mark could not have been made by the side of the support track, or the top or bottom of the support track. The witness mark had to have been made by contact with the aft (blunt) end.

From the location of the witness mark – it is on the front side of the stiffener bracket – we know that when the contact with the support track occurred the liberated flap section had to have been moving in the up (forward/retract) direction.

In normal operations, when the flaps are completely retracted (up), the support track does not extend far enough into the seal pan to reach that stiffener bracket. What all this tells us is that at the exact instant when the flap section was liberated from the rest of the flap, it was thrust toward the full up (retract) position, and in fact, it retracted to where it was beyond the normal full up (retract) position.

We also know that the flap section was flailing (swinging wildly) as it travelled up (towards retract) because we can see the numerous points of contact damage it

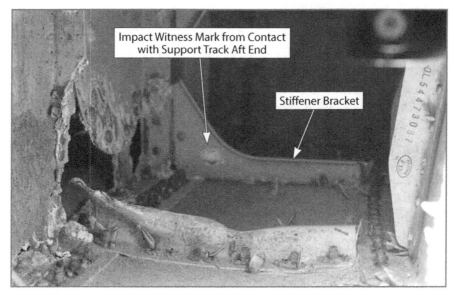

FIGURE 25 Impact Witness Mark from Contact with Support Track Aft End

created – they are evident inside the seal pan (see Figure 21). And of course, the location of the witness mark (in Figure 25), down in the corner of the stiffener bracket, confirms that the seal pan was misaligned with the support track.

Here is yet another piece of evidence to confirm that the flaps were extended as the airplane entered the water. Again, this evidence is based on witness marks that you can clearly see for yourself. In Figure 26 we can note the distinct difference in the relative positions of the outboard flap and flaperon for when the flaps are retracted (up), or extended (down).

The annotations (see "Stiffener Locations") in Figure 26 point to three very robust structural pieces in the wing. With the flaps retracted (up), we can see that the forward end of the flap, and those stiffeners, would be adjacent to each other. We can also see that with the flaps extended, the forward end of the flap, and the stiffeners, would not be adjacent to each other.

We know that when MH370 entered the water, there was a significant spanwise crushing force created along the trailing edge of the wing. This force crushed the flaperon and flap into each other. If MH370's flaps had been retracted (up) when that spanwise crushing occurred, there would most certainly have been three very distinct imprints into the seal pan endplate (the endplate is shown in the insert in Figure 26). Specifically, the three imprints would be evident at the locations annotated by the three arrows. Conversely, with the flaps extended (down), there would be no such imprints.

The photo in the insert of Figure 26 shows that there are no such imprints on the recovered seal pan endplate. You can get another view of that same area

69

(as annotated by the three arrows) in Figure 14. Clearly, there are no imprints from the stiffeners. Again, this is evidence that you can see for yourself. It is not difficult to analyze or to understand. The absence of these stiffener imprints provides even more proof that MH370's flaps were extended (down) when the airplane entered the water.

With the above information, we are now able to document and analyze the failure sequence for the recovered flap section. Just to review, specific to the recovered flap section there are four pieces of evidence that confirm that the flaps were extended (down) when the airplane entered the water.

First, there is the shredding/shattering damage at the trailing edge (see Figure 9). That damage could only have happened if the flaps were extended (down) while being pulled through the water.

Second, there is the black smudge mark imprint on the seal pan endplate (see Figures 11, 14 and 16) that could only have been made at that location if the flaps were fully extended (down). It would be impossible for the flaperon to make that imprint, at that location on the endplate, if the flaps had been retracted (up).

Third, we have the witness mark evidence inside the seal pan (see Figure 21), which proves that the flap section had been violently moved from flaps extended (down) to flaps retracted (up). The way that evidence was created proves that the starting position for the flaps had to have been flaps down.

Fourth, we see the absence of damage on the front part of the seal pan endplate (see Figure 26), which proves that the flaps were not retracted (up) when the airplane entered the water. If the flaps had been retracted (up), there would have been three distinct imprint zones created by spanwise crushing with the wing structure at that location.

You can clearly see the overwhelming physical evidence that proves the outboard flap (and all the other flaps) entered the water in a fully extended (down) position. The trailing edge damage on the recovered flap section occurred while the airplane was skimming across the ocean surface during a controlled ditching. The extended (down) flap contacted the swells and waves, causing the water to be directed down and around the trailing edge. It was these water-hydraulic forces that caused the trailing edge damage.

At the same time, the force exerted by the water would be trying to push the flap towards up (retracted). The flap could not retract (up) because it was hydraulically locked down (extended) through the flap hydraulic actuators.

As was confirmed earlier, when the right wingtip entered the water there was buckling in a wave pattern along the right wing's trailing edge. We also confirmed there was downward buckling at the location where the recovered flap section severed from the rest of the flap. The severing resulted from the combined forces of the buckling, and the water pressure pushing against the bottom (front) of the flap as the extended (down) flap was being dragged through the water.

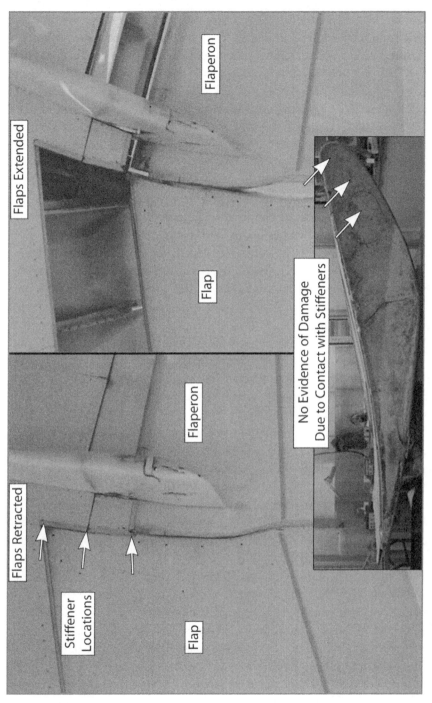

FIGURE 26 Showing the Absence of Specific Damage – Proof that the Flaps Were Extended (Down)

The flap section severed from the rest of the flap at the exact same time that the flap mount broke (see Figure 22). With the flap mount no longer holding the severed piece in the extended (down) position, the severed piece was now free to flail. The only thing left holding it to the wing was its attachment to the carriage assembly inside the seal pan.

Remember the architecture involved: the carriage assembly was still attached to both the flap section, and the support track. The support track was still attached to the trailing edge of the wing. But of course that attachment setup was not designed to hold the flap to the wing; its only purpose was to steady the inboard end of the flap. In no way could that attachment be compared to the robustness of the connection through the flap mounts.

The evidence tells us what happened. At the instant the flap mount broke, the flap section was no longer being held in the extended (down) position. The water force against the bottom (front) of the flap section drove the flailing piece towards the retracted (up) position. Because the flap section was flailing, the seal pan was now in total misalignment with the support track. This misalignment is what caused all the up (forward movement) witness marks inside the seal pan (see Figure 21).

We saw the evidence that showed the flap section was forced all the way up until there was contact inside the seal pan between the blunt end of the support track and the stiffener bracket (see Figure 25). As we confirmed earlier, this up movement actually went beyond the normal fully retracted (up) position for the flaps.

Coincident with the flailing flap section being driven up (to beyond retract), the force of the water was separating it from the wing. In relation to the forward-moving wing, the water forces were holding the flap section back. It was this relative movement (the wing going forward, and the flap section going rearward) that pulled the support track and carriage assembly out through the hole in the front of the seal pan. This is what caused the rearward movement witness marks inside the seal pan (see Figure 21), and the damage around the access hole (see Figure 20).

Even though the flap section was flailing, the fact that it was pulled rearward in relation to the wing allowed it to escape in near pristine condition. It remained relatively undamaged because it never made any contact with the trailing edge of the wing in front of it. As we saw earlier (in Figures 9 and 19), the flap section retained its aerodynamic shape, with almost no damage to its leading edge, or to its upper or lower surfaces.

Using wreckage analysis, the next section explains the physical evidence that confirms MH370 was in a wings level attitude (not banked to either side) when the airplane approached and entered the water.

From our previous analysis, we know that the trailing edge erosion damage on the flaperon, and the shattering damage on the trailing edge of the outboard flap, had already occurred prior to the right wingtip entering the water. Knowing that, we need only look at the simple geometry of the airplane to see that it could not have been in anything other than a wings level attitude as it entered the water.

If you are not able to visualize that, use your paper airplane to experiment. If you try to fly your airplane to land on a relatively flat surface (i.e., the ocean surface) in a banked attitude (a turn), you can clearly see the wingtip would be first to strike the water, and that wingtip would undoubtedly dig in to the water.

There would be no way to create the erosion and shattering damage on the trailing edges of the flaperon and flap section after a wingtip had already struck the water first. For the trailing edge damage to occur, the airplane had to have made the first contact with the water with its wings level (see Figure 8).

We will now look at some additional evidence that MH370 entered the water in a wings level attitude, that is, the airplane was landing straight ahead. It was not turning with the wings in a banked attitude. This confirming evidence comes from two other pieces of wreckage that were recovered (see Figure 27).

Figure 27 shows the in-service locations of these two pieces of wreckage from MH370. Each had separated from one of two identical wing panels, one on the top of the left wing, and one on the top of the right wing. Note that the identical panels are immediately in front of the flaperon on each wing. Also note that each piece separated from the exact same location on its panel – the aft outboard corner.

From an investigation perspective, it is remarkable that these two pieces of wreckage are basically mirror images of each other (I will refer to them as twins). One is from the right wing, and the other is from the left wing.

We know that only twenty confirmed pieces of wreckage have been recovered from MH370. For a curious investigator, a basic question would be: why would two of only twenty pieces be twins from opposite sides of the airplane? Could that be coincidence, or is there a logical explanation for it? We will see below that there is a logical explanation, and it is based on solid investigation analysis.

When the investigators from the official investigation looked at these two pieces, they probably thought they were typical of small pieces that would be created during a high-speed diving crash. Apparently, the significance of these twin pieces was not recognized.

Here is some basic analysis. If there had been a high-speed diving crash, and these twin pieces had actually been liberated in that type of crash, the force of the crash would have liberated at least hundreds of other pieces with similar construction. Each one of the many hundreds would have had an equal chance of floating to a shoreline. It is very far-fetched to believe that from all these hundreds of similar pieces, only these two twin pieces floated all the way to a shoreline. What are the odds of that happening? I would say close to zero. That is not a realistic scenario – it makes no sense.

Here is the reality. There never were large numbers of similar pieces created, because there was no high-speed diving crash. What happened was that these twin pieces were created by a similar and specific failure mechanism, and it happened during a pilot controlled ditching. They were liberated from the airplane because of where they were located – directly in front of each flaperon. The analysis to support this conclusion comes next.

Much of the evidence presented to this point has been supported by witness marks that you can easily see. These twin pieces have no specific witness markings that show exactly how they were liberated. However, this gives us an opportunity to see how sound investigation analysis can lead us to a logical and very supportable conclusion.

Here is that analysis. We can see in Figure 27 that the failure mechanism for each of the twin pieces was that they were simply ripped free from the wing panel they had been a part of. In wreckage analysis terms, we call it ripping and tearing damage. Such ripping and tearing damage can happen in a high-speed diving crash, but we know that MH370 was not subjected to that type of event.

That tells us that the ripping and tearing damage that liberated our twin pieces must have resulted from abnormal forces in the wing structure surrounding each piece. Logic tells us that each twin piece was liberated in the same way. Each twin piece was exposed to an equivalent abnormal force, and that force was created at about the same time, and in the same way, in each wing.

The next investigative step is to look at what is inside the wing structure beneath each of these twin pieces. Mounted inside the wing at these locations is the support structure that holds the flaperon to the back of the wing. There are also support structures for the hydraulic mechanisms that move the flaperons up and down.

In a controlled ditching scenario, these are the support structures that would be holding against the tremendous force of the water trying to drive each flaperon towards its up (retracted) position. As each flaperon got deeper into the water during the controlled ditching, those water forces would become exceptionally strong. Extraordinary stresses would build up in those localized areas of the wing structure in front of each flaperon.

It is logical to conclude that each of the twin pieces broke free from the top of its wing because of the stress concentrations and wing-skin distortions in those very localized locations. It is also logical to conclude that the localized stress concentrations and wing skin distortions were created when the extended (down) flaperons were being dragged through the water. This is all very logical analysis.

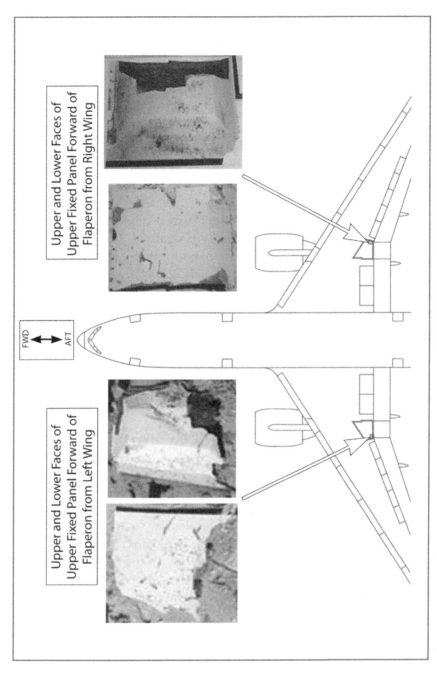

Upper and Lower Faces of Upper Fixed Panel Forward of Flaperon from Right Wing

Upper and Lower Faces of Upper Fixed Panel Forward of Flaperon from Left Wing

FWD
AFT

FIGURE 27   Depicting Two Wreckage Pieces that are Basically Twins – One From Each Side of the Airplane

There is no logic that could explain these twin pieces in a high-speed dive scenario. The localized forces that liberated these twin pieces could not be created if the flaperons were streamlined to the water flow in an up (retracted) position, regardless of the speed the airplane entered the water. To create these localized forces on the support mechanisms, and resultant stress risers and wing-skin distortions, both flaperons had to have been extended (down), as they would be with the flaps extended (down).

We saw earlier that the right flaperon broke free from the right wing because of the spanwise crushing forces created along the right wing's trailing edge (combined with the water forces). That happened when the airplane's right wingtip dug into the water.

In the controlled ditching event, there would have been no equivalent spanwise crushing force on the left wing, because the left wingtip did not dig into the water. It is reasonable to assume that the left flaperon sustained equivalent erosion damage to its trailing edge, but it probably did not break completely free from the wing because it was not subjected to the same spanwise crushing forces.

The takeaway from this analysis is that it provides further proof that MH370 entered the water with its wings level (the airplane was not banked). This analysis shows that a wings-level water entry is the only scenario that explains how these twin pieces were created. And of course this analysis also adds to the proof that MH370 entered the water with its flaps fully extended (down).

With the above information, we can now review and add to the narrative about how MH370 entered the water. We know that as it approached the water surface, the airplane was in a controlled ditching attitude, with the wings level (not banked). We know that the engines would touch the surface first, and they would be ripped off.

Next, the extended (down) flaps/flaperons would start to contact the swells and waves (see Figure 8). The airplane would still be travelling at a near flying/landing speed. This is when the trailing edge damage we see on the recovered flaperon and flap section occurred. Although we do not have proof, it is reasonable to assume that similar damages occurred on the trailing edges of all the flap system pieces, as they all would have been extended (down).

As the airplane settled further into the water, the water pressure against each extended flaperon caused the localized forces that popped the twin pieces from the tops of each wing. As the airplane slowed, the right wingtip dipped and was struck by a wave/swell, and it dug into the water. This is what created the spanwise loading that compressed the trailing edge of the right wing. It was this spanwise loading, combined with water forces, that caused the recovered right flap section, and the right flaperon, to break free from the airplane. No such spanwise loading would have occurred on the left wing, which explains why similar pieces were not recovered from the left wing.

Wreckage Pieces From Inside the Fuselage

There is more that can be learned from the recovered wreckage pieces. In this section, we will assess the three individual pieces of wreckage that have been identified as being from inside the passenger cabin of MH370. The fact that they were recovered proves that during the controlled ditching, the fuselage must have been breached. That would be the only way for those pieces to escape from inside the airplane. They had to have passed through an opening (breach) in the fuselage structure.

Figure 28 shows each of the three interior wreckage pieces.

The top photo in Figure 28 is part of the R1 door on MH370 – the most forward door on the right side of the airplane. The middle photo is a piece of cabin interior panel; it could not be determined exactly where it had been installed in the passenger cabin. The bottom photo is a seat back trim panel; the panel that encases the In-Flight Entertainment monitor. It could not be determined which passenger seat it had been attached to.

The small size of these pieces, and the fact that they escaped from inside the fuselage, has led many people to believe they could only have been created in a high-speed diving crash. Taken in isolation, these three pieces might fit with a high-speed dive scenario, but to conclude that based on these three pieces alone is a huge stretch. We know there is overwhelming evidence to reject a high-speed diving crash, so we know that there must be another explanation for how these small interior pieces escaped from the fuselage.

Fortunately, given our knowledge of how the airplane entered the water, it is not difficult to determine

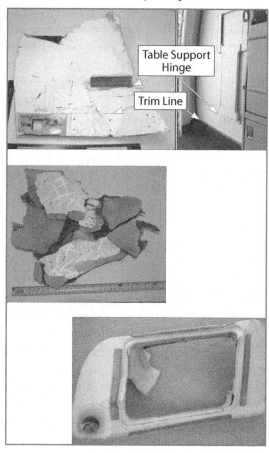

FIGURE 28 The Identified Interior Wreckage Pieces from MH370

what the source was for the damage (inside the fuselage) that produced these pieces, and to explain how they escaped from the fuselage. Investigation analysis tells us that it happened as follows.

We know that there was significant spanwise loading that was compressing the trailing edge of the right wing into the fuselage. From our experiment earlier with the paper airplane, we can see that the greatest concentration for this compression would be at the aft wing root (the aft wing root is where the trailing edge of the wing connects to the fuselage; see Figure 1 and Figure 13).

As this compression along the trailing edge of the right wing built up, the crushing pressure against the fuselage would eventually be too much for the fuselage structure to resist. The structural design of the airplane simply does not account for massive compressive loads into the fuselage structure at that point. Eventually, the wing root structure would have crushed through into the fuselage. If that happened (and it likely did happen), it would create a breach (hole) in the fuselage through which the small interior pieces could escape.

A breach into the fuselage at the wing root would account for at least two of the three small interior pieces shown in Figure 28. Those pieces could easily have been torn free as part of the crushing contact inside the fuselage.

The piece from the R1 door could have been dislodged by contact with something, such as a food cart, during the massive deceleration during the ditching. That piece could also have exited the same hole at the wing root, but that is not likely.

There is a more plausible scenario for that piece escaping. It is more likely that the R1 door simply popped open. With the right wingtip dragging in the water, the front part of the right wing root would be under a massive tension load, which would be trying to rip the wing out of the fuselage. The aft part of the wing root would be under an equally massive compression load, pushing it into the fuselage, as described above.

There would be substantial distortion in the fuselage, not only from these wing root stresses, but also from the loads applied when the front part of the airplane entered the water. This distortion could cause the R1 door to pop open.

Once the door opened, the interior of the door would be subjected to the forces of the water rushing by during the ditching. That could easily explain how a piece of the interior of the R1 door could break free.

There is no specific witness mark evidence on this R1 door piece to show exactly what happened to create it, or to show us exactly how it managed to exit the fuselage. A proper investigation analysis requires that we use already confirmed evidence to guide us to the most likely scenario.

In this case, we have already determined the sequence up to where extraordinary compression forces were acting on the fuselage at the right wing root. We also know, from the existence of the interior wreckage pieces, that the fuselage had been breached.

We can look at the timing for when the breach must have occurred. There is no reason to believe that the fuselage had been breached prior to when the right wingtip dug into the water. There is no logic to thinking that a breach could occur very late in the controlled ditching sequence, after the airplane had already slowed to a near stop. Therefore, it is logical to conclude that the breach occurred exactly as described above, at the time the wing root broke through into the fuselage.

It is important to remember here that the overriding question about what happened to MH370 has already been answered – the pilot intentionally ditched the airplane. What we are doing now is simply ensuring there is a reasonable explanation for the other evidence that is available. We are showing how all of the pieces of recovered wreckage can be accounted for in our scenario of an intentional pilot controlled ditching.

Wreckage Pieces from the Tail Section

Among the pieces of wreckage that have been recovered are three small pieces that broke free from the tail structure. Again, there is no direct physical evidence to confirm exactly how they broke free. One thing we know for certain is that they broke free as part of the controlled ditching process.

There are two possibilities to explain how they broke free. One possibility is that they were simply torn free by the force of the water against the tail during the controlled ditching. Another possibility is that they were dislodged when they were struck by some piece that had broken free of the airplane.

If something did strike the tail, the most likely candidate would be the right wing. There is a reasonable chance that the damage at right wing root was sufficient to cause the wing to completely separate from the fuselage. It could then have travelled aft into the tail.

It is also possible that some individual piece from the right wing (such as a section of the flap) broke free and struck the tail.

This is another instance where there is insufficient evidence to confirm one way or the other what the forces were to dislodge these tail structure pieces. However, the existence of these pieces cannot be used to cast doubt on the controlled ditching scenario. We must remember that we already have definitive proof as to what happened to MH370. Regarding these pieces, we simply need to show that they are not at all inconsistent with a pilot controlled intentional ditching scenario.

The Nine Additional Recovered Wreckage Pieces

So far, we have analyzed eleven of the twenty wreckage pieces that have been confirmed as coming from MH370, and tied each of them to a controlled ditching event. That leaves nine additional pieces that must be accounted for. In this section, we will evaluate their importance, and look to see what information they can provide.

As reported by the official investigation (and I agree), there are no significant witness marks on any of these nine pieces. However, they are informative because their in-service locations on the airplane have been identified.

Figure 29 identifies nineteen of the twenty pieces that have been confirmed as having come from MH370, and indicates where they came from on the airplane. The piece that is not identified in Figure 29 (which is sourced from the Ministry of Transport of Malaysia) is their piece number 12, which they identified as being a part of a bottom panel from the wing or horizontal stabilizer (see the location of the horizontal stabilizer in Figure 1). The nine pieces that we must account for, as identified by the numbering system used in Figure 29, are as follows: #'s 2, 4, 6, 7, 10, 12, 18, 20 and 27.

One thing that is immediately notable from an investigation perspective is that every one of the nine pieces is from an external location on the airplane, where it is vulnerable to damage from a controlled ditching event. Also, as discussed earlier, it is interesting to note a lack of items from inside the airplane, such as personal effects, luggage, or other items from the cargo area. You would expect to see lots of floating material from the cargo after a high-speed diving crash.

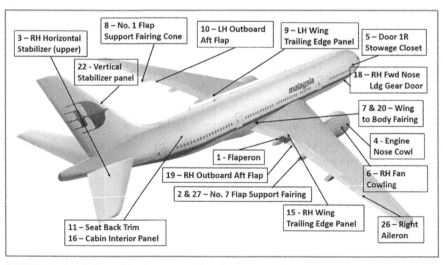

FIGURE 29 Depiction of the Recovered Wreckage Pieces from MH370

The only pieces recovered that were identified as being from the interior of MH370 are the three that we have already addressed (above). It should be noted that other small pieces have been found, but none of them have been positively identified as being from MH370. It is possible that some of them might be, and if so, they would be consistent with being produced during a pilot controlled ditching, the same as the other pieces we have analyzed.

Let's look at the remaining nine pieces of recovered wreckage. Three of the nine are pieces dislodged from the flap system (piece #'s 2, 10 and 27). We have already discussed how a flaps-extended (down) controlled ditching would make such pieces highly vulnerable to becoming dislodged. We would expect to see those pieces.

Two of the nine remaining pieces were dislodged from the engine cowlings (piece #'s 4 and 6). Engine cowl pieces would be particularly susceptible to being dislodged during a controlled ditching, given that the engines would be first to enter the water. We would expect to see those pieces.

Another two of the nine are pieces from what is called the wing-to-body fairing (piece #'s 7 and 20). As implied in the name, these fairings are located at the meeting point between the wing and the fuselage (at the wing root). One fairing piece was positively identified as being from the right wing. The in-service location of the other is unknown, but we could speculate that it is also from the right wing. We know about the crushing that happened at that precise location during the controlled ditching, so we would expect to see those pieces.

One of the nine pieces was identified as part of the right-hand nose gear forward door (piece # 18). In a controlled ditching, that area of the airplane's forward underside would be subjected to extreme water forces. There would be a high potential for this nose gear door piece to be dislodged during a controlled ditching.

The last one of the nine pieces is from a bottom panel on either a wing, or the horizontal stabilizer, which is part of the tail (piece #12). A piece from either of those locations would be subject to the forces we have already discussed as being present during a controlled ditching event.

From an investigation perspective, the information from these nine pieces is very powerful. When we include these remaining nine pieces, we have now analyzed all twenty of the identified pieces recovered from MH370. We have shown that each of the twenty can be directly connected to a controlled ditching event.

As an investigation exercise, we can now try to connect these twenty pieces to a high-speed diving crash scenario. As we know, a high-speed diving crash would have created hundreds (and realistically thousands) of pieces of floating debris. Many of those pieces would be at least as buoyant as the twenty pieces that have actually been recovered.

Staying with our investigation exercise, let's assume there actually was a high-speed diving crash. We would start with thousands of buoyant wreckage pieces floating in a debris field on the ocean surface. Let us now say that we could magically go to the floating debris field, and tag the exact twenty pieces that have been recovered and identified. Now we wait for several months, to see what happens, as these thousands of pieces float randomly in the ocean.

Let us assume that over the many months, most of the original thousands of pieces deteriorate, and sink to the bottom. But logic (and physics) tells us that there would still be many dozens, and more realistically hundreds, of pieces that would continue to float for just as long as the twenty that we magically marked (the ones that made it to a shoreline and were recovered).

What do you think the odds would be that of the hundreds of pieces that remained floating, the only pieces to float to a shoreline would be the exact twenty pieces that we magically marked? These are the same twenty pieces that we have directly connected to a controlled ditching event. There are no other pieces. You do not have to be a specialist in probability theory to recognize what the odds are against that happening. Essentially, the chance of that happening is zero.

The reason that no high-speed dive type pieces have been found is that they were not created in the first place. There was no high-speed diving crash. The reason that only pieces linked to a controlled ditching have been found is that they were the only ones that were created. We have seen the evidence that explains how they were created.

Once again, this type of analysis should not have been a challenge for the official investigation. You can judge that for yourself. It is simply common sense.

We can assess why the official investigation was unable to figure it out. As explained previously, from very early in the investigation they became fixated on their unpiloted airplane theory. That theory was reinforced when their experts pointed to what they believed to be electronic evidence of a high-speed dive.

It appears they were influenced by that bias when they looked at the few recovered wreckage pieces. Apparently, they saw the twenty pieces as a random assortment that had washed ashore from what was once a much larger debris field, made up of small floating pieces. They reasoned that only a few pieces made it to shore because all the others had eventually become water saturated, and sank to the bottom.

Apparently, they never recognized that all of the pieces that were being recovered would fit nicely into a pilot controlled ditching scenario. It seems they had no inclination to look at all the recovered pieces collectively to see if there was a scenario other than their own that could explain how they were created.

Description of the Pilot Controlled Ditching Event

All the information above gives us an even clearer picture of what happened to MH370 as it approached and then entered the water. During the descent, the engines were running normally. Towards the bottom of the descent, the pilot extended the flaps to full down. The pilot put the airplane in a slightly nose-up (landing) attitude, with the wings level. The two engines touched first, and they were ripped away.

Then, the trailing edges of the extended (down) flaps (on both wings) started to contact the swells and waves. The airplane would still be travelling at a near flying speed. This contact with the water surface is what caused the trailing edge erosion and shattering damage we see on the recovered pieces from the flap system (the flaperon, and the section of the outboard flap).

As the airplane settled further into the water, the water pressure against the two flaperons caused the twin (mirror image) pieces to pop off the wings, as discussed above. The airplane continued to slow, and eventually the right wingtip entered a wave/swell, causing the right wingtip to dig into the water.

As explained earlier, the drag on the right wingtip is what created the span-wise loading that crushed the flaperon and outboard flap into each other. It was this crushing force, combined with the water forces, that caused them to break free. No such spanwise loading would have occurred on the left wing, because its wingtip did not dig into the water. This likely explains why similar pieces from the left wing flap system were not recovered (because they never broke free from the wing).

The extensive damage at the right wing root caused a rupture in the fuselage, creating a pathway for pieces from inside the fuselage to escape. It is likely that the most forward door on the right side of the fuselage popped open. It is possible that the entire right wing broke free from the airplane. It was either the entire right wing, or some significant piece from the right wing, that damaged the tail and dislodged pieces from there.

Water would have very quickly invaded into the fuselage through these holes, and the airplane would have quickly started to sink. The inrushing water would have allowed only a minimum number of pieces from inside the fusel-age to escape.

Although this would have been a violent sequence overall, very few pieces of floating debris would have been created. This is the sequence that accounts for all the wreckage pieces that have been recovered. A high-speed diving crash scenario simply does not fit.

We must reinforce the significance of the flaps being extended (down) when MH370 entered the water. Only a deliberate selection by a pilot can extend the flaps. The fact that MH370's flaps were extended (down) proves that a pilot was controlling MH370 at the end of its flight, and proves that the official investigation is not correct in their contention that MH370 was an unpiloted airplane.

The position of the flaps also proves that the airplane did not run out of fuel. To extend (lower) the flaps requires both a functioning hydraulic system, and a functioning electrical system. The flaps are electrically actuated, and hydraulically driven.

Some people will point out that the B777, like other transport category airplanes, has an auxiliary power unit (APU) that is capable of supplying both hydraulic and electrical power, even if the engines are not running. More will be included about the APU later, but for now, let me assure you that you do not have to understand the complexities of the B777's backup systems to accept that the flaps cannot extend unless the pilot intentionally selects them down.

It is also not a stretch to accept that the pilot would want to have full control of the airplane all the way to the surface by having engine power available. He would have made certain that he had enough fuel to get the airplane on the water. It is much easier to control the airplane with the engines running than to try to control it without the engines running, especially if your intent is to conduct a controlled ditching.

Summary of the Physical Evidence That Shows Flap Configuration

Listed below are thirteen descriptions of physical evidence that prove the flaps were extended when MH370 entered the water. In my opinion, each one of the thirteen is sufficient, all on its own, to prove there was no high-speed diving crash.

From an investigation perspective, and even from a common sense perspective, when you look at these thirteen physical pieces of evidence collectively, they provide overwhelming and indisputable proof that MH370 entered the water in a flaps-extended (down) pilot-controlled ditching.

Here are the thirteen descriptions of the physical evidence that confirm that the airplane's flaps were extended (down):

1 – The basic pristine condition of the recovered flaperon (see Figure 4)

If the airplane had entered the water in a high-speed diving crash, the entire airplane would have been destroyed in the blink of an eye. It would be impossible for the flaperon to have maintained its normal curved shape at its leading edge, and to have maintained its normal curvature along its upper and lower surfaces.

2 – The erosion damage along the trailing edge of the flaperon (see Figure 7)

The damage along the trailing edge of the flaperon could not have occurred in a high-speed diving crash, where the flaps would be in a streamlined (trail)

84

position. The erosion damage resulted from the force of water being directed down and around the extended (down) flaperon as the flaperon was being pulled through the water during a controlled ditching event.

3 – The uncrushed (basically pristine) condition of the recovered piece from the right outboard flap (see Figure 9 and Figure 19)

Similar to the flaperon, it would be impossible for the flap section to have maintained its normal curved shape at its leading edge, and its normal curvature along its upper and lower surfaces, if the airplane had entered the water in a high-speed diving crash.

4 – The shattering damage along the trailing edge of the recovered flap section (see Figure 9)

Similar to the flaperon, the damage along the trailing edge of the recovered flap section could not have occurred in a high-speed diving crash, where the flaps would be in a streamlined (trail) position. This shattering was caused by multiple impacts on the trailing edge of the extended (down) flap as the airplane settled into the swells and waves during a pilot-controlled ditching event.

5 – The compression fracture in the end plate of the flap section, caused by spanwise crushing forces that crushed the flap and the flaperon together (see Figure 12)

The compression fracture was caused by the spanwise crushing forces along the trailing edge of the right wing. Spanwise forces could not have been created in a high-speed diving crash. The spanwise crushing forces were created when the right wingtip dug into the water during a pilot-controlled ditching event.

6 – The "V-shaped" black smudge witness marking on the outside of the seal pan endplate (see Figures 11, 14 and 16)

This smudging was created when the severe spanwise force caused crushing between the outboard end of the flaperon and the endplate. The location of the smudge witness marks shows the relative positions of the flaperon and the outboard flap when the crushing occurred. This witness mark evidence is proof that the flaps were extended when MH370 entered the water.

7 – The damage around the edges of the entry hole for the flap support track to extend into the seal pan (see Figure 20)

The support track and carriage assembly caused that damage when they were pulled out through the hole. This could only happen if the wing was going forward, while at the same time the flap was being held back. The flap was extended (down) and was being pulled through the water. It is impossible for that scenario to be created in a high-speed diving crash.

8 – The witness mark damage inside the seal pan that shows the flailing flap section moved in two different directions – at one time moving forward, and at another time moving aft (see Figure 21)

A high-speed diving crash would explosively rupture the wing in a tiny fraction of a second. The entire airplane, with all its pieces, would have only massive forward momentum. In a high-speed diving crash scenario, it is physically impossible for the flap to have moved so that it could create damage while travelling in two opposite directions.

9 – The significant inward bend in the flap's push/pull rod that proves it was experiencing a significant spanwise (inboard) bending load before it finally broke (see Figure 22 and Figure 23)

Such a spanwise force could never be created in a high-speed diving crash.

10 – The overlapping gouging on the recovered flap section that confirms the presence of compressive buckling loads along the fracture line (see Figure 24)

The spanwise loading caused the trailing edge of the wing to buckle in a wave pattern. It was buckled downward at the seam line where the recovered flap section ultimately broke free from the rest of the flap. In a high-speed diving crash, it would be impossible to create such spanwise loading and compressive buckling.

11 – The end-point damage at the outboard leading edge corner of the recovered flap section, caused by the downward buckling at the location of the eventual fracture line (see Figure 24)

This end-point damage confirms the presence of compressive buckling loads that would be impossible to create in a high-speed diving crash scenario.

12 – The impact witness mark left by the aft end of the flap support track on the stiffener bracket inside the seal pan (see Figure 25)

The location of the witness mark (it is both off-centre, and beyond the normal full up position of the support track) proves that when this mark was made, the liberated flap section was flailing and moving towards up (retracted). In order for this flap section to move "up" at the instant it was liberated, it had to have started in a down (extended) position.

86

13 – The pristine condition of the front (forward) part of the seal pan end-plate (see Figure 26)

Had the flaps been fully retracted, the spanwise crushing would have left three significant crushing imprints at the front of the endplate. The front of the endplate would have crushed into the three robust structural pieces inside the wing. The complete absence of this type of damage is proof that the flaps were not retracted.

As stated earlier, each of these thirteen physical pieces of evidence is, by itself, sufficient to prove the flaps were fully extended (down) when MH370 entered the water. When they are looked at collectively, they leave absolutely no doubt.

5
DISMISSING
OTHER SCENARIOS

In this chapter, we will examine some of the various scenarios that have been put forth as potential explanations for the disappearance of MH370. The objective here is to describe and compare the various scenarios, and to examine and assess their validity. This process will allow us to zero in on the most likely scenarios, and to eventually recognize that there is only one that is consistent with all of the known facts.

In teaching aircraft accident investigation courses, I demonstrate various methods that can be effective in organizing and analyzing the known facts. The circumstances of the individual event will dictate which methods are most useful.

For MH370, a demonstrative way to present and evaluate the various scenarios is to use a simple table – a grid pattern, with horizontal columns and vertical rows. Page size constraints in this book limit the number of rows and columns that can be displayed. However, it is possible to show by way of illustration how this method works. In a classroom, the number of columns can be expanded to include whatever scenarios the class participants suggest.

I acknowledge that the table does not contain all the known facts, or all the suggested potential scenarios. I also acknowledge that it is possible to debate which of the boxes deserve a checkmark (✔). Please do not get distracted by the contents of the table. I ask you to follow along and allow it to demonstrate how this analysis tool works, and to show how it can be useful in an actual investigation analysis situation.

The left column (going down) is used to list the known facts. The top row (going across) is used to list potential scenarios that could have caused the event. The checkmark (✔) in the intersecting boxes means that it is possible/probable to connect the known fact back to the potential lead event.

In working with this methodology, you must consider that when you have gathered all the known facts, there is only one scenario at the top that will allow a checkmark (✔) in every box in its column, and that is the scenario that actually happened. If you have an empty box in the column under a particular scenario, then either you have an incorrect fact (you have to reassess its validity), or that scenario did not happen, and can be disregarded.

As we examine various scenarios below, you may find it helpful to construct your own table for MH370 where you can add more columns for other potential scenarios, and a longer column of known facts. You are doing real investigation work when you have to decide what you will add as a known fact. Seeking out and validating facts is the most fundamental activity in professional investigation work.

In the end, for each potential scenario, the table will show either an unbroken column of check marks, or a dead end with empty boxes.

This is a good opportunity to explain what leads to so much of the inaccurate writing and commentary regarding aircraft accidents. What typically happens is that people come up with a scenario that (if they used a table like the one on the right) would string together a number of checked boxes. Then, they present that scenario as a possibility for what happened. What they fail to recognize is that if they were actually using a table that had all of the known facts included, their scenario would reach a point where they would get to empty boxes. People who do not use a method, such as the table on the right, do not recognize that the empty boxes are there.

Here is an example of how that happens, using the scenario of a cockpit fire in MH370. Is it possible that a catastrophic cockpit fire could disable a transponder? The answer is yes – so give that a checkmark. Is it possible for such a fire to disable an airplane's communication systems? The answer is yes – so give it a checkmark. Is it possible that the airplane could make several turns at high altitude with an ongoing fire? The answer is yes – so give it a checkmark. Is it possible for an oxygen leak to increase the severity of an in-flight fire? The answer is yes – so give that a checkmark. Is it possible for a fire to cause an airplane to depressurize? The answer is yes – so give it a checkmark. Is it possible for a fire to disable a flight crew? The answer is yes – so give that a checkmark.

With all these checkmarks lining up, the individual doing the research becomes convinced they have discovered what happened, or at the very least what could have happened. In the absence of proof showing where the empty boxes would be in the table, people can come to believe that their scenario "probably did happen", and convince others.

It is important to realize that someone who is presenting a scenario that theoretically could happen is not actually providing proof that it did happen, no matter how meticulous his or her research might appear. In the absence of accurate factual information from the official investigation (which is what we see from the MH370 investigation), any theory with reasonable looking logic is as good as the next one.

	Potential Lead Events				
Known Facts	Onboard Fire	Rapid Decompression	Passenger Hijack	Electrical / Mechanical Failure	Pilot Intentional Act
MH370 Departs	✔	✔	✔	✔	✔
Climb to FL350	✔	✔	✔	✔	✔
Switch to next frequency	✔	✔	✔	✔	✔
Transmit "Good Night…"	✔	✔	✔	✔	✔
Transponder signal disappeared	✔				✔
Scheduled ACARS reports stopped	✔		✔	✔	✔
Airplane made several turns at high altitude	✔		✔	✔	✔
ACARS reappeared					✔
Airplane flew southbound for some 6 hours					✔
Entered the ocean at relatively low speed					✔
Entered the ocean in a controlled ditching attitude					✔
Entered the water with the flaps down					✔

Inevitably, unless someone is working with the scenario that actually happened, their scenario will have boxes that cannot be given a checkmark. Some cannot find the empty boxes for their scenario because they choose to disregard any fact that does not fit with it. Others do not discover the empty boxes because they simply do not have the expertise to recognize what all the facts are, or how to assess them.

No matter what method is attempted to assess the facts, it can only work if the inputted facts are correct. The official MH370 investigation team went astray when they accepted the unpiloted airplane theory as a fact. They went further astray when they calculated that before entering the water the airplane was in an unpiloted high-speed dive. Then they went completely astray when they incorrectly assessed that the flaps were retracted (up) when the airplane entered the water.

In examining theories that have been proposed for what happened to MH370, it is not my intention to single out any particular individual for their attachment to any specific theory. From what I have read, for any given theory that has been proposed by an individual, there are many others who have expressed their support or opposition.

Below, I have attempted to group the collective thinking on each general theory into one descriptive narrative – for the purpose of assessing its validity.

The Theory of an Onboard Fire

Some people support the theory that an onboard fire disabled MH370. Various origins for a fire have been proposed, including lithium-ion batteries in the cargo compartment, a malfunctioning windscreen heater, and an oxygen leak in the cockpit.

As part of the MH370 investigation, it would be standard practice for the investigators to look at the potential for an onboard fire. In particular, investigators would examine all potential fire initiation sources, looking for any potential threats to the safety of the airplane. If any safety deficiency is identified, they have a responsibility to make that deficiency known, so that proper protections can be put in place.

For MH370, working through a standard investigation process can dismiss a fire scenario as the lead event. We can work through that process here – the same process that would be followed by a professional investigation team. We will look first at the potential for a lithium-ion battery fire to be the lead event; that is, the first event in a chain of events that led to the disappearance of MH370.

Our fire scenario starts with the initiation of a fire in a cargo compartment containing the batteries. Our objective, as we work our way through this scenario, is to try to connect this fire initiation to the first known anomaly in MH370, which was the disappearance of the airplane's transponder signal. In other words, for this hypothesis to be validated, we must be able to construct a chain of events that link the cargo compartment fire directly to the transponder signal failure. That is standard investigation practice.

The cargo compartments are below the passenger cabins, down in the belly of the airplane. We know that in the B777, all the cargo compartments have very sophisticated fire protection. The protections include both aural and visual fire warnings in the cockpit, and fire suppression and containment systems built into the cargo compartments.

So now we have an investigation question – if there was a lithium-ion battery fire in a cargo compartment, is it reasonable to assume that the cargo compartment fire detection system would detect that fire almost immediately, and activate the aural and visual warnings in the cockpit? The answer is yes – it is reasonable to accept that a lithium-ion battery fire in a cargo compartment would very quickly produce aural and visual warnings in the cockpit.

We know that when the pilot was making his final radio transmission, there were no fire warnings in the cockpit. We know that because the pilot's voice was very calm, and he had not been alerted to any fire. We know that on the ATC recording of that call, there was no sound of an aural fire warning in the background. Therefore, it is reasonable to conclude that there was no lithium-ion battery fire in a cargo compartment when the pilot was making his last radio transmission.

The transponder signal from MH370 disappeared from radar screens less than two minutes after this final radio transmission. So here is another investigation question: is it possible that in less than two minutes, a fire could ignite in a cargo compartment, and propagate to where the heat from that fire could disable the transponder? Let me give you the quick answer – no. That is not a reasonable assumption, as explained below.

Within the official investigation team, all potential fire scenarios would be examined in great detail. Here is a condensed version of how professional investigators would conduct their analysis.

Investigators would know that there was a large shipment of lithium-ion batteries on board MH370. They would know that lithium-ion battery fires are self-sustaining, and that they burn very hot, and that they are not easily extinguished. They would know that the cargo compartment was designed to withstand a flame source of 1,700°F for at least five minutes. They would assess how long a lithium-ion battery fire would take to penetrate through the purpose-built fire-resistant cargo liner in the B777. If they were unsure (after checking the certification testing documents), they would conduct their own testing.

From a safety perspective, if they had any doubt about the ability of the fire protection systems in the cargo compartment to function as designed, they would recommend recertification. If they felt that the certification standards were not high enough, they would recommend enhanced standards.

They would know that a lithium-ion battery fire could not be extinguished by the cargo compartment's halon fire suppression system. For the purpose of following the scenario (by assuming it actually happened), they would accept that a lithium-ion battery fire actually escaped from the cargo compartment. They would then look for potentially flammable materials in the B777 that could support the spread of the fire from the area of the cargo compartment to the nearest electrical wiring needed to allow the transponder to function.

They would be aware that no critical wiring needed to support services in the cockpit (including the transponder) are located in the vicinity of the cargo compartments. They would know that before the fire could affect any critical wiring, the fire would have to spread extensively into other parts of the airplane, including into critical wiring in the forward section of the airplane.

They would do testing to determine how long it would take for a propagating fire to spread all the way to where it could affect critical aircraft wiring, including wiring that supports the functioning of the transponder.

They would assess the type of wiring used to power the transponder. In particular, they would test the wire's resistance to heat and fire. They would determine that the protective covering on such wiring is exceptionally resistant to heat and flames. In certification, aircraft wires are assessed as pass/fail by being exposed to the flame from a Bunsen burner. The testing is very stringent.

Investigators would know that before a fire could cause the loss of the transponder signal in MH370, the fire would have had to burn through the protective covering on the wire to expose the copper conductor inside. The exposure of the copper conductor would cause the wire to short circuit, and trip a circuit breaker. They would know that even after the fire had propagated all the way to where the wiring was located, it would take at least several minutes for the fire to burn through the wire's protective covering.

Again, the above is only a summary of how investigators would assess the potential for a lithium-ion battery fire to have been the lead event in the disappearance of MH370. It is easy to see that such a scenario does not fit with the known facts. It would take much longer than two minutes for a fire to start in a cargo compartment and spread to where it could expose the conductor of a critical wire supporting the operation of the transponder.

We can look at another potential fire scenario that gained some support. In this scenario, the fire started from a defect in the windshield. The fire initiation was followed by pilot actions, and system defects, that led to the fire being greatly intensified by the introduction of oxygen.

Heat from the fire caused the circuit breakers for the transponders and communications radios to trip, and drove the pilots from the cockpit. The fire eventually caused a breach in the pressure vessel, and the airplane depressurized. Through all this, the autopilot remained functional. The pilots, who were injured, could not make the airplane descend to a survivable altitude, but they were able to aim the airplane south over the ocean. Then, they succumbed to hypoxia.

This is a textbook example of a scenario (as discussed previously) that can generously be viewed as "theoretically possible". Some might view it as improbable, because it is based on a number of complicated actions and factors that had to come together simultaneously. But in the absence of proven alternatives, some people view it as credible.

In reality, there is not a single piece of hard evidence to prove that this scenario actually happened. It is the same for any of the other fire theories. Each of these theories depends on there being an unpiloted airplane at the end of the flight. The evidence proves that none of these fire theories are possible, because at the end of the flight the pilot was alive and functional, and he was controlling a fully functioning airplane all the way to the ocean surface.

The Theory of a Passenger Hijacking

Some people support the theory that MH370 disappeared after a passenger or passengers on board hijacked it. Once they gained control, they dictated and controlled each subsequent event, all the way to the end of the flight.

The case for a passenger hijacking is very weak, and the arguments against it are strong. However, there is no specific evidence to unequivocally reject it. Therefore, to investigate it we must follow a standard investigation process. There are at least three different hijacking scenarios that have support from some MH370 investigation enthusiasts.

The first is a scenario where a passenger or passengers onboard MH370 hijack the airplane by gaining access to the cockpit.

The second scenario involves one or more passengers gaining access to the airplane's onboard flight computers, which are located in the electronics and equipment bay. The compartment housing the electronics and equipment can be accessed from inside the passenger cabin through a hatch door in the floor aft of the cockpit. This scenario suggests that hijackers entered the compartment, and used sophisticated electronic equipment they had smuggled on board to take control of the airplane.

The third scenario involves remote hacking into the airplane. The perpetrators remotely hacked into the airplane's flight management systems, thereby controlling and navigating the airplane remotely.

Let us first look at the possibility of a hijacking by a passenger or passengers who were on the airplane, and gained access to the cockpit. (For simplicity of writing, I will refer to one male hijacker – the investigation process would be the same if there were more than one hijacker.)

Passenger doors on airline airplanes are exceptionally robust. Once the cockpit door is closed for flight, the only way the door can be opened is if a pilot unlocks it from inside the cockpit.

The first thing to be looked at when assessing a potential passenger hijacking is timing. We must show a direct link between our "cause" (in this case the hijacker), and the first known anomaly (the disappearance of the transponder signal). Remember that it was less than two minutes from when the pilot made his final radio transmission until the transponder signal disappeared. In fact, the first transponder anomaly occurred only one minute and six seconds after the pilot's final radio transmission. We must assess the likelihood of a hijacker being able to access the cockpit, and disable the transponder, in that short of a timeframe.

Another factor in this passenger hijacking theory is that the hijacker would have to be very knowledgeable about airplane operations, and have very specific knowledge about operating a B777. The hijacker would have to know that disabling the transponder would make the airplane disappear from radar. Also, the hijacker would have to know how to keep the pilots from taking subtle actions that would alert air traffic control about the hijacking.

The investigation authorities claimed that they conducted background checks on everyone on board MH370. They contend that no one on board had a background that would give them specific knowledge about airplane operations. If that is true, then the only two people on board MH370 who were capable of operating and flying the airplane were the two pilots. Therefore, in this passenger-hijacking scenario, we must assume that the hijacker forced the MH370 pilots to keep flying the airplane, and to follow his orders.

Let us return to how this hijacker could gain access to the cockpit. We can envision how the cockpit door might have been opened momentarily. Perhaps a pilot opened it to allow access by a flight attendant. Perhaps one of the pilots had to leave the cockpit to use the washroom. Remember the timing – the hijacker would have had only about one minute to gain access through the cockpit door, and then to gain control of the airplane, and then to have the pilots shut down the transponder, and then to have the pilots start a turn to reverse course.

Because of the timing, you would have to assume that when the cockpit door was opened, the hijacker was nearby, and ready to attack. Only people in the first class section of the airplane would be in a position to have quick access to the cockpit door area. The hijacker would have to be nearby, and watching for that door to be opened. Most certainly, the cockpit door would not have been opened if any unexpected passenger were lurking nearby.

In this passenger hijack scenario, here is what would have to happen within a timeframe of something less than one minute. The hijacker would have to force his way into the cockpit. Then the hijacker would have to gain full control over both pilots. Then the hijacker would have to order the pilots to disable the transponder. Then the pilots would have to comply. At the same time, the hijacker would have to order the pilots to immediately start a turn to reverse course, and the pilots would have to comply.

Remember that in this scenario, these activities took place at the exact location where there was a handoff between air traffic control agencies. At this location, air traffic control monitoring of the airplane was at a minimum. It would be a tremendous coincidence if a ready and waiting hijacker were fortunate enough to have the cockpit door open at that most suitable location.

You would have to assume that the hijacker knew enough about airplane systems to know that the transponder is the electronic link that allows air traffic control to see the airplane on radar. You would have to assume that the hijacker knew how to ensure that the pilots actually complied with his request, and switched the transponder off. You have to assume that the pilots complied with the hijacker's request, and they did so because they knew that he would recognize it if they simply switched to another transponder, or otherwise failed to comply. The pilots would know of many ways to send information from the airplane to ATC that would be unknown to an unsophisticated hijacker. Nevertheless, nothing more was heard from MH370.

You would have to assume that the hijacker also knew specifically to order the pilots to disable the ACARS communications system. Remember that in the factual sequence of events, the ACARS failed to send a scheduled routine position report that should have been sent about 16 minutes after the transponder signal disappeared. In this passenger-hijacking scenario, we can assume that the hijacker ordered the pilots to disable the ACARS, in addition to disabling the transponder.

Disabling the ACARS in the cockpit is not something that pilots would ordinarily or routinely do. There is no reason to do so. There is not one specific switch to turn the ACARS off. To disable ACARS requires very specific knowledge, and more than one action by the pilot. This suggests that if there was a passenger-hijacker dictating the events, that hijacker was someone who had sophisticated knowledge about the operations of a B777, and in particular about the ACARS.

From the factual sequence of events, we know that about one hour after the ACARS first missed its expected routine update, it came back online. However, it did not return to full functioning, in that it still failed to transmit its expected routine reports. Once it was disabled, there is no way for the disabled ACARS to come back online unless someone turns it back on. Again, turning the ACARS back on cannot be done by simply selecting an ON switch; it requires specific and sophisticated knowledge, and more than one action. There is no reasonable explanation for why a hijacker would order the pilots to turn the ACARS off, and then allow them to go through the process of turning it back on.

We then must assume that the hijacker dictated the specific route that the airplane followed, starting with the initial turn to reverse course, and including its other turns, and its eventual long flight to the southern Indian Ocean. We then must assume that the hijacker ordered the pilots to carry out a controlled ditching on the ocean surface, and we must assume that the pilots complied.

As I stated earlier, this hijack theory cannot be dismissed by definitive and unequivocal evidence. Each element of it is theoretically possible. However, when assessed from start to finish, it is highly unlikely that all of the elements described above could come together without intervention.

To get an even greater appreciation for how unlikely a passenger-hijacking scenario is, we need only look at how much less complicated it would be for a pilot to take the actions instead of a hijacker.

It is not realistic to propose that a hijacker had the ability to direct the pilot to accurately fly any specific course, especially one designed to avoid military radars. Even if you accept that premise, it is not realistic to propose that in the dark of night a hijacker would be able to follow the airplane's progress to ensure it was going to where he had directed the pilots to take it.

It would be easy for the pilots to confuse the hijacker, and take the airplane in a different direction. If they were hijacked, the pilots would want to attract attention from ATC. They would want to fly over land, and in particular, would want to avoid flying so far from land that they would have no option but to end up in the ocean.

In this proposed passenger-hijacking scenario, the pilots would still be flying the airplane. The pilots would most assuredly take action once they recognized that without their intervention the airplane would end up in the ocean. They would not sit idly by and allow the airplane to fly for hours out to sea. The pilots would have options.

One option would be to cause the airplane to suddenly depressurize. They could do this with a single switch selection. Rapid decompression would allow an opportunity to neutralize the hijacker. Given the pilots' familiarity with the airplane and the cockpit, and the hijacker's lack of familiarity, the pilots would have a distinct advantage. They would be able to get themselves on oxygen, and continue to function. Meanwhile, in the confusion, the hijacker would quickly succumb to hypoxic symptoms.

Of course, this depressurization would also affect the passengers, but once the hijacker was neutralized the pilots could quickly restore the pressurization and descend the airplane to get oxygen levels back to where hypoxia would no longer be an issue.

Another option for the pilots would be to disable the cockpit lighting, and manually fly the airplane into a condition with high G-forces, or negative

G-forces. Again, the pilots would have a distinct advantage in the darkness and confusion. This could be done in combination with depressurization.

I will not attempt to list all of the options that might be available to pilots in this type of passenger hijacking scenario. There are two things that are certain. One is that any pilot, including the pilots of MH370, would take whatever actions were available and necessary to avoid flying the airplane to an unavoidable fatal outcome. The second is that if MH370 were a passenger hijacking, it would not have ended with the pilots conducting a controlled ditching in a remote part of the southern Indian Ocean.

The Theory of an Electronic Hijacking

We can now look briefly at the other two proposed hijack scenarios we had mentioned earlier. There is support for a theory that some passengers hijacked the airplane by gaining access to the airplane's onboard flight computers, which are located in the electronics and equipment bay (under the floor below/behind the cockpit). The hypothesis is that the hijackers took control of the airplane by using sophisticated electronic equipment they had smuggled on board.

Every professional airplane accident investigator, and every professional pilot, and every professional airplane designer, and every professional maintenance engineer, and everyone familiar with operating airplanes, knows that this hijack scenario is completely unrealistic. Computers in the electronics and equipment bay are used only for maintenance diagnostics. They are designed to function only when the airplane is on the ground.

To be able to fly and navigate the airplane from the electronics and equipment bay would require a complete redesign of the airplane, and a complete rebuild of its flight control systems. It is both naive and preposterous to propose that such a major redesign could be replaced by some type of electronic wizardry hacked into a system that could not possibly react to it.

For this scenario to be true for MH370, one would have to accept that passenger-hijackers forced their way into the electronics and equipment bay shortly after take off, and they were able to work there without challenge or interference, and that the pilots failed to notice their devious activities while they were reprogramming the cockpit functions and flight controls, and that the pilots therefore did not inform air traffic control of any irregularities, and that the pilots made no attempt to divert the flight to get the airplane back on the ground, and that within something less than thirty minutes after take off, the hijackers were ready to disable the transponder, and to take complete control of the airplane from the pilots, and that the hijackers caused the airplane to reverse course, and that in that short timeframe they somehow reprogrammed the airplane to fly a circuitous route to avoid radar detection, and then to fly far out into the southern Indian Ocean, and then to extend the flaps, and then to carry out a controlled ditching. You would have to accept that the passenger-hijackers knew that their efforts would result in their own deaths, and the deaths of everyone else on board.

I am compelled here to add some comments about wild theories such as this electronic hijacking theory. It is frustrating to watch as these types of stories gain traction on the internet, and get media attention. Even though they have no basis in fact, they garner interest because they provide intrigue and entertainment, especially when attached to a tragic event such as MH370. At the same time, they are a source of misinformation that can needlessly concern people about the safety of air travel.

A tragic consequence of stories like this is that they have real and lasting negative effects on the families and loved ones of those who perished in the airplane. I have witnessed this consequence first hand, and the damage is real, and it can be heartbreaking. There are versions of this particular hijacking theory that claimed that the airplane landed safely at some remote location, and that the airplane's occupants were captive, but alive.

Regardless of whether the motivation to present such a story is personal gain, or notoriety, or a misguided attempt to inform, it is inhumane and shameful to promote such an implausible scenario while ignoring the mental anguish it could inflict on such vulnerable people.

The third hijack scenario mentioned earlier involves remote hacking into the airplane, where the perpetrators gained control of the airplane's flight management systems from some remote location. The discussions above about onboard hijacking should suffice to discredit any remote hijacking theories. Such theories can be dismissed, their only value being as entertainment for conspiracy theorists and fans of science fiction.

The Theory of a Mechanical or Electrical Malfunction

Some people support the theory that MH370 disappeared because of a mechanical malfunction. In a thorough investigation, investigators always look for potential mechanical deficiencies in the type of airplane under investigation. They look for any deficiency that could pose a risk to the airplane type (in this case, the entire fleet of B777s). In any investigation, the search for such deficiencies can lead to safety improvements, even if they find a deficiency that they are unable to connect directly to the event.

To investigate the likelihood of a mechanical malfunction as the lead event in the disappearance of MH370, we must follow a standard investigation process. As has been stated previously, there is a difference between finding a potential safety deficiency (something that theoretically could happen), and connecting that potential deficiency to the actual sequence of events that led to the loss of the airplane.

We can refer back to the table with the known facts in the far left column, and the potential lead events across the top. You will recall that only the column with the true and actual lead event at the top will allow a checkmark (✔) in every box.

The first known anomaly with MH370 was the disappearance of the transponder signal. At the same time, the airplane started its turn to reverse course. Our investigation to look for a potential mechanical malfunction lead event must find a way to connect the mechanical failure directly to these first anomalies.

It is easy to imagine how a mechanical or electrical malfunction could have caused the transponder signal to be disrupted. For example, hypothetically, there could have been an electrical short circuit, or simply a failure in one of the components supporting the operation of the transponder.

It is not so easy in this hypothetical scenario to imagine why the pilots were unable to restore the transponder signal. The B777 has a significant amount of redundancy in its transponder system. The airplane has more than one transponder, and there are numerous paths for electrical power to reach each transponder.

To continue our investigation process, we can look past the first known anomaly to the next known events, and examine them in the context of the hypothetical mechanical or electrical malfunction. We know that after the transponder signal stopped, the airplane remained flyable. We know this because the airplane continued to fly for several more hours.

We know that regardless of the nature of the hypothetical malfunction, the pilots were not completely disabled. We know this because they not only reacted to the transponder malfunction by reversing course; they reprogrammed the navigation system to execute several turns.

With this hypothetical mechanical or electrical malfunction, we also have to account for the fact that the pilots were still functioning at the end of the flight, where there was an intentional and controlled ditching. For any hypothetical mechanical or electrical malfunction to be valid, it must be able to be connected not only to the first known anomaly, but also to each of the subsequent events, all the way to the end of the flight.

The proponents of a mechanical or electrical malfunction have theorized that the same (initial) malfunction that caused the transponder signal to disappear also caused the airplane to depressurize. The representative storyline goes like this – the malfunction occurs – the first reaction by the pilots was to turn the airplane around – the performance of the pilots was degraded by hypoxia – they mistakenly reprogrammed the flight management system to follow the new track – and then the pilots succumbed to hypoxia.

This sequence, of course, would lead to MH370 being an unpiloted airplane. We have proof that the unpiloted airplane theory is not correct. The fact that MH370 was under the full control of a pilot at the end of its flight puts to rest any potential that the entire sequence of events started with a mechanical or electrical failure.

In my view, there is no need to go through any more of the numerous other theories involving a mechanical or electrical fault as the lead event in the disappearance of MH370. The storyline for each of these theories includes the pilots being disabled, and there being an unpiloted airplane, and we know that is not true.

The Theory of a Bomb, or Military Action

There is support for a couple of different theories involving direct damage to the airplane. One theory involves military action (the airplane was damaged by military firepower). The other involves direct damage from a bomb that exploded on board.

Once again, to prove that one of these theories is correct requires that it be tied directly to the first known anomaly, which was the transponder going offline (less than forty minutes into the flight).

To try to account for the subsequent navigation of the airplane (after the bomb/missile), these theories describe some sort of valiant struggle by the (injured) pilots to maintain control of the airplane. Supposedly, the pilots were able to guide it through the various known turns, including the turn southbound to fly over the ocean. The airplane was depressurized because of the damage, and the pilots eventually succumbed to hypoxia, leaving an unpiloted airplane.

Those types of scenarios are invalidated by the proof that there was a controlled ditching at the end of the flight. We could stop with that, but I will offer more on this issue to continue with the theme of showing how investigation analysis is done.

Even without the evidence of a controlled ditching, there are other factors working against these bomb/missile theories. For example, investigators would take into account that the airplane remained flyable, and the autopilot remained functional, despite the extensive damage that was supposedly inflicted to the airplane.

To accept either of these hypotheses, you would have to believe that the autopilot could remain engaged and functional, while at the same time the transponder (with all its backups), and all the communication radios (with all their backups), and the ACARS, had all been disabled by a missile or bomb.

To believe that is a very big stretch. You would have to believe that engaging an autopilot is somehow comparable to engaging a mechanical lever, akin to engaging the big lever that starts the rotation of a carousel ride. Autopilots do not work like that. A modern autopilot is a sophisticated computer, which is connected to a network of other computers and sensors that feed it with complex and vital information. If invalid inputs are introduced, or are perceived anywhere in the system, the autopilot's default is to disconnect. It defaults to "OFF" to prevent it from following potential bogus inputs. It cannot be re-engaged until the bogus inputs are eliminated by a maintenance technician.

Investigators would also assess the soundness of that part of the bomb/missile theory that proposes the pilots steered the disabled airplane to where it could do no harm. That theory plays to the dramatic scene of a pilot steering a crashing airplane away from a schoolhouse, but it does not in any way fit the context of a bomb/missile scenario for MH370.

In such a scenario, the MH370 pilots would have stayed over land, where there would have at least been a chance of finding an airport, or of crashing with survivors. There is no way they would have intentionally set their airplane on a course over the ocean, on a course to certain death. Without any question or doubt, they would have taken any and every action within their power to try to save their passengers.

With that, any scenario involving military firepower, or an onboard bomb, can be dismissed. No such theory can account for what actually occurred regarding MH370, and especially for the deliberate pilot actions that were taken.

Various Other Theories

There are other theories that have gained support, but for each of them, counter-arguments can be made using logic similar to that used above. There would be little to gain by detailing each of the proposed theories, but to satisfy the curiosity of some readers, I will touch upon a few of them.

Terrorism can be dismissed using the same investigative logic used to dismiss the hijacking theories. The use of some form of secret weapon can be dismissed using the same investigation logic used to dismiss a bomb, or a military shoot down.

Some people support theories based on witnesses seeing lights on the airplane as it flew over in the darkness. Anyone who stole the airplane, and was smart enough to turn the transponder and ACARS off, would also be smart enough turn off all the outside lighting. In the darkness, there would be no lights for witnesses to see.

There is no chance the airplane landed at the United States airbase of Diego Garcia, or at any of the many other landing places that have been named; such propositions are not worthy of comment.

An abduction of the airplane by individuals carrying out some sinister government plot can be dismissed using the same sound logic used to dismiss abduction by aliens. That same sound logic can be used to dismiss the theory that the airplane was sucked into a black hole. If you choose to disagree with using sound logic, you can look to the many experts who use none of it.

6
THE INVESTIGATIVE
USE OF SATELLITE DATA

In the pilot's plan to make MH370 disappear without a trace, he assumed that once the airplane flew out of radar coverage there would be no way for anyone to determine where it went. What he failed to account for was a communications system designed into the airplane that automatically stayed in touch with a satellite communications network.

Over the six-plus hours that MH370 flew southbound, this satellite communications network generated seven contacts between the airplane and the satellite, basically one per hour. These contacts are known as "handshakes".

The following is a depiction of seven rings, calculated from the handshakes, as shown in the ATSB report titled *The Operational Search for MH370*, dated 3 October 2017 (Page 12):

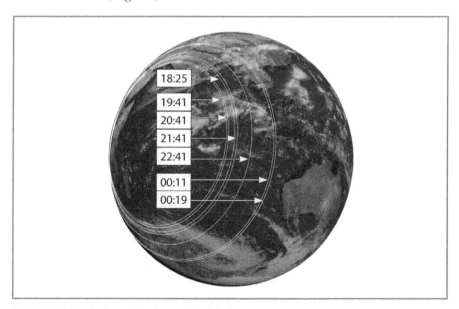

FIGURE 30 Depiction of the Seven Handshakes

After the accident to Air France 447, which crashed into the ocean off the coast of Brazil in 2009, the data in these handshakes was modified to allow for a rudimentary form of track reconstruction. In the simplest terms, the airplane and the satellite communicate using electronic signals. The speed of the signal transfer is known, and the position of the satellite is known. With that information, experts can calculate the airplane's location based on the time it takes for the signals to travel back and forth. Fortunately, the pilot's actions to cut off all electronic contact with MH370 failed to fully shut down the airplane's capability to contact that system.

A dedicated group within the official investigation team, led by the *Australian Defence Science and Technology (DST) Group*, conducted an analysis of these handshakes. Using sophisticated and groundbreaking methods, they were able to reconstruct the basic path of the airplane as it flew to the southern Indian Ocean. The results of their work were used to direct the official investigation's search for wreckage. Resources were directed to the areas of the ocean identified as most likely to contain the wreckage.

For those who are interested in scrutinizing the work of this group, they have produced a number of detailed reports that are available through the *Australian Transport Safety Bureau* website (www.atsb.gov.au). In those reports, they explain their logic, and procedures, and calculations. They also include the assumptions they used in producing their results.

Two assumptions that were used in their calculations were: 1) MH370 was flying as an unpiloted airplane, with no pilot input; and 2) the airplane eventually ran out of fuel at high altitude, and descended at high speed into the ocean. As we have seen in this account of what happened, there is proof that these two important assumptions were not correct.

There is an appearance of "certainty" (my word) in the DST group calculations. I use the word "certainty", because with their assumption of an unpiloted airplane, they are able to make mathematical calculations, and mathematical calculations produce definitive results. The results can be accurate, provided they are calculated using accurate inputs.

By using their unpiloted airplane scenario, the DST group could assume that because the airplane was flying on autopilot, with no pilot inputs, it maintained a constant altitude and airspeed during the flight to the south. Based on an assumed power setting and altitude, they could calculate where the airplane would run out of fuel. Then, using a B777 simulator, they could establish how far the airplane would be able to travel after the fuel was exhausted. Finally, by factoring in the calculated airplane tracking information they had extracted from the handshakes, they could establish boundaries to define the specific search areas.

While the official investigation's active search for wreckage was ongoing, the investigation authorities publicly presented a high degree of confidence in their assumptions and calculations. They expressed a high degree of "certainty" about where they were searching, and the likelihood of finding the wreckage.

The DST group's unpiloted airplane theory is invalidated by the proof that there was a pilot controlling the airplane. There was a pilot-controlled descent, and a pilot-controlled ditching. Both of these events occurred before the airplane ran out of fuel. If you accept the evidence that a pilot was controlling a functional airplane, then you have to accept that the DST group calculations are not valid.

Unlike the autopilot, the pilot can (and did) take independent actions. Without the "certainty" provided by the unpiloted airplane assumptions, it is not possible to use the handshake data to predict where or when the airplane started to descend, or which direction it travelled during its descent, or its airspeed during the descent, or its rate of descent.

During the flight south, the pilot could have changed altitude, or changed the power setting. That would affect fuel consumption, and maximum range. It is not possible to know how much fuel remained in the tanks after the last handshake. Therefore, it is not possible to accurately predict how long, or how far, the airplane flew after the last handshake. It is not possible to establish the time the airplane entered the water.

With the uncertainty introduced by a pilot-controlled scenario, it is not possible to predict a touchdown location for the airplane, other than in very general terms encompassing a wide area.

There is no doubt that the DST group calculations prove that MH370 flew a track to the southern Indian Ocean. The drift modelling completed after the discovery of the wreckage pieces confirms that is where MH370 is. The basic track line established by the DST group most certainly points to the general area of the southern Indian Ocean where the wreckage of MH370 is located. Unfortunately, that basic track line, pointing to a general area, is the extent of what can be determined using the handshake data alone.

When (and I guess if) the official investigation accepts that MH370 was a pilot controlled event, perhaps the experts in the DST group, or in some other group, will use this (new to them) information to restart their calculations. They would have to come up with new assumptions about the flight south. They would have to account for extensive variables regarding altitudes, and airspeeds, and power settings. They would have to assume the pilot could have changed anything, at any time.

It is reasonable to assume that the pilot was aiming to ditch the airplane within a specific target area on the ocean surface; at a location where his pre-planning told him the underwater topography would be least conducive to the wreckage being discovered. Any new calculations would have to make new assumptions, based on a fully flyable airplane. Assumptions would have to be made about where the pilot started to descend from a cruise altitude, and about his rate of descent, and about his airspeed during the descent, and about where and when he made any turns.

The pilot wanted to ditch the airplane with the least possible damage. To prepare for the controlled ditching, he could have turned the airplane into the wind. He could have made a heading change to account for the waves and swells.

The DST Group

I will now address an aspect of the relationship between the investigation authorities and the DST group that I believe requires particular focus. There is at least the possibility that the investigation authorities knowingly influenced the work of the DST group to support a particular outcome. Was the official investigation looking to the DST group for extra ammunition to support their selection of the search zone? Were they looking for credibility to justify their ongoing search?

In their document titled *MH370 – Search and debris examination update* (dated 2 November 2016), the ATSB referenced conclusions from the DST group that were very helpful to their ongoing wreckage search. Specifically, the DST group (incorrectly) gave the official investigation hard data pointing to a high-speed dive. This evidence was convincing, because it appeared to come from independent experts, who were working with hard evidence. (Supposed) hard data now (unjustifiably) confirmed what the official investigation had been saying; that MH370 entered the water in a high-speed diving crash.

The official investigation framed it this way: that the final satellite communications to and from the aircraft showed a high and increasing rate of descent. The DST group's hard evidence showed a rate of descent approaching twenty-five thousand feet per minute – basically, a classic spiral dive.

In that same 2 November 2016 update, where the official investigation released this hard data, they also released the results of their examination of the recovered flaperon, and the recovered section from the right outboard flap. The witness mark evidence they found on both the flaperon and the flap section (incorrectly) confirmed that both had been retracted (up) during a high-speed impact.

These two quite astounding claims: 1) that they had hard data showing a steep dive; and 2) that they had physical evidence of flaps retracted, were particularly influential in countering the views of those (including me) who were saying that MH370 was a pilot controlled event.

I knew at the time they released their update in November 2016 that the two claims they were making were clearly false. I remember wondering, as I still do, if everyone on the investigation team believed them to be true. Surely some members of the investigation team knew that what was being called hard data was in fact derived data. Hard data comes directly from something like a flight data recorder. All their results were calculated within significant margins of error, using assumptions and interpretations.

In any event, the release of this supposedly unimpeachable information from the ATSB was widely covered in the media, and generally accepted, and it supported the ATSB's logic for their ongoing search for wreckage.

There will be more on this later, but first we can look at how the DST group came to support the inaccurate conclusion of a high-speed dive. Thankfully, we can do so without delving too deeply into the complex science they undertook. Here are the basics.

To keep our task manageable, we will not go through the complexities of challenging the accuracy of the DST group's calculations that produced the first six handshake locations. Many people have already challenged the accuracy of the track line they came up with for the flight southbound. However, for simplicity, we will not challenge that. Instead, we will start from handshake #6. (Actually, I should say "the location of" handshake #6, but that makes for awkward writing, so I will drop the words "the location of").

The time between handshake #6 and handshake #7 was only eight minutes. The official investigation contends that during those eight minutes, the airplane ran out fuel, and the engines stopped. To be more specific, they claim the engines stopped about six minutes after the airplane passed handshake #6. If you do the math, this is two minutes prior to the airplane reaching handshake #7.

The engines drive the electrical generators that supply electrical power to the airplane. With no electrical power, the communications unit that was producing the handshakes would shut down.

A quick reminder here: the B777 has an auxiliary power unit (APU), which is a small jet engine located at the tail end of the fuselage. In the air, it is normally not running. It is used only as a backup, but when it is in use it can supply power to (among other things) the airplane's electrical and hydraulic systems.

The official investigation believes that when the engines stopped from fuel exhaustion, the APU automatically started. It is designed to do that. The APU uses the same fuel as the engines, but it has access to the last bit of fuel in the tanks – fuel that is not available to the engines. The official investigation contends that the start-up of the APU restored electrical power to the communications unit, and when the communications unit rebooted it sent a log-on request, and that is why handshake #7 happened.

To the official investigation, the reboot of the communications unit is proof that there was an automatic start-up of the APU, and the automatic start-up of the APU is proof that the engines had stopped, and the stopping of the engines is proof that the airplane had run out of fuel.

We know that none of that actually happened, but from a theoretical/technical perspective, it certainly is possible for it to happen. What seems to have made fuel-starvation even more believable to the official investigation is that the (supposed) start-up of the APU happened very close to the time that they had calculated for when the airplane would run out of fuel (based on their assumptions).

According to the DST group calculations of the handshake data, the unpiloted airplane was already in a descent before it reached handshake #7. Naturally, they attributed this descent to the loss of engine power. They assumed that by the time the airplane passed handshake #7, it was already out of control.

The next part of their calculation (to determine where the airplane crashed) was to insert the results of Boeing's no-engines simulator testing. This allowed them to establish the parameters for their wreckage search area. To them, everything was logical, and everything fit together.

The problem is that all of their calculations were based on the unpiloted airplane theory. We know that the unpiloted airplane theory has been disproven by the evidence presented in this book. We know that the pilot was controlling what happened to the airplane, from start to finish. We know that the pilot was controlling the airplane all the way until it entered the water.

Explaining the Satellite Data

With no flight data recorders, it is not possible to determine the actual sequence that the pilot followed to prepare for the controlled ditching. However, it is certainly possible to come up with potential sequences that would account for the satellite data that was interpreted by the DST group as showing an uncontrolled high-speed dive. The following describes one such sequence.

Let us assume that the pilot used the autopilot during the flight south. This is a very reasonable assumption. Let us accept that the airplane followed the route calculated by the official investigation that took the airplane to handshake #6. As mentioned, I believe the accuracy of that track can be challenged, but let us accept it for now.

As he approached the end of the flight, the pilot would be keenly aware of the airplane's fuel status. As part of his pre-planning for this event, on other flights he would have paid particular attention to watching fuel consumption numbers. He would know almost to the minute how much fuel (flying time) he had remaining. Given his intention to ditch the airplane with the least possible damage, he would have had absolutely no reason to allow the airplane to run out of fuel prior to reaching the water surface.

We can imagine that as the airplane was nearing the location for handshake #6, the pilot would be preparing for the controlled ditching. (I remind you that the pilot would have no concept of any handshakes – he thought he had shut off all contact with the airplane – I refer to the handshake locations here only to allow a comparison with the official investigation's version of events.)

110

Whatever happened to precipitate handshake #7 (we will accept for now it was a reboot of the communications unit), it could not have been a result of the APU automatically starting after the engines stopped. We know the engines did not stop. Therefore, the reboot of the communications unit must have been a direct result of some action taken by the pilot.

From an overall investigation perspective, it is not necessary to figure out exactly what precipitated the reboot of the communications unit to come to a conclusion about the loss of MH370, but for general interest, we can speculate.

In preparing for the controlled ditching, perhaps the pilot was reconfiguring the airplane's electrical system to restore some electrical function he had shut down. Or perhaps he was changing some electrical system to a different power source. In his reconfigurations, perhaps he somehow managed to interrupt, and then restore, electrical power to the communications unit.

In my view, it is more likely that the pilot started the APU intentionally, and then switched some electrical services to the APU. Perhaps this caused power to the communications unit to be interrupted and then restored, causing it to reboot.

There is logic for why the pilot might start the APU for a controlled ditching. Perhaps he wanted to make sure he would still have electrics and hydraulics if the fuel to the engines ran out at the last minute. Having the APU already running would protect against the risk of losing electrics and hydraulics during the controlled ditching. He would know that the plumbing inside the airplane's fuel tanks would allow the APU to have access to the last bit of residual fuel in the tanks; fuel that the engines cannot access.

Another possibility is that the pilot started the APU as part of his plan for maintaining control during the aircraft's entry into the water. He would know that in a controlled ditching, the engines would touch the water first, and they would stop immediately from water ingestion. He would know that the APU, which is higher up in the tail, would keep running after the engines stopped. The APU would maintain electrical and hydraulic functions for the final few seconds, potentially giving him more control throughout the controlled ditching.

These are only two of the many such scenarios that are possible. Once all this evidence that proves there was a controlled ditching is widely accepted, interested people will most certainly present other potential scenarios.

The DST group misinterpreted the data from handshake #7. The following describes (in very basic terms) how they concluded MH370 had entered a steep descent.

First, based on data they had for previous handshakes, they projected what the data should look like for handshake #7. They made that handshake #7 projection based on there being no alteration in the airplane's flight path (the airplane continuing to fly straight and level from handshake #6 to handshake #7).

Then, they compared their projected data to the actual data they got for handshake #7. The data they got for handshake #7 was significantly different from what they had projected, so they knew that after passing handshake #6, there must have been a change in the trajectory of the airplane.

To assess what that change might be, they started with their assumption of an unpiloted airplane. Therefore, they assumed that the airplane did not change direction between handshake #6 and handshake #7. With that assumption, only a steep descent could explain the significant alteration in the data. And of course, that conclusion fit nicely with their assumption that the airplane had run out of fuel. It was totally incorrect, but it all fit nicely together.

There are other potential explanations for the "unexpected" handshake #7 data. Here is one example. At a point somewhere near handshake #6, the pilot entered a deliberate and controlled descending turn. This was part of his positioning for the controlled ditching. A change of direction was not accounted for in the DST group assumptions. So instead of the data showing an airplane entering into a steep and increasing rate of descent, the data could be reflecting an intentional controlled descent, combined with a change of direction. Again, this is just one potential explanation – there are many others, but we need not speculate further.

I will now refocus back to the issue of whether the official investigation authorities might have unduly influenced the work of the DST group. It is interesting to note that the DST group did not independently develop an end of flight scenario based solely on the satellite data. In fact, it would have been impossible for them to do that. There was simply not enough data available.

It was the ATSB investigators who gave the DST group the end of flight scenario they were to use. In constructing the full end of flight scenario, and in calculating their search zones, the DST group was instructed by the official investigation to assume that MH370 was an unpiloted airplane. They were told that both engines had failed, first one, and then the other.

They were instructed to incorporate the results of the simulator testing into their calculations. The simulator testing informed them that the airplane would react to the asymmetric engine failures by entering an out-of-control steep descent. They were told what rates of descent the airplane would achieve, and how long the airplane would stay in the air, and how far it could travel.

It was with this pre-conditioning and instruction from the official investigation that the DST group interpreted the data at handshake #7. If they looked for other scenarios that would fit with the data, any such alternate scenarios were dismissed. That is unfortunate, but understandable, given that they were instructed to look at only one scenario. It seems that the DST group's task in assessing the end of the flight was simply to determine how out-of-control the airplane was during its dive into the ocean.

Whether deliberate or not, the interactions between the official investigation and the DST group resembled a mutually beneficial support circle. The DST group was able to prove the robustness of their science when they were able to produce, from unbiased "hard data", a result that confirmed exactly what the official investigation says actually happened. The official investigation benefited by being proven correct through an independent scientific process that used "hard data".

The problem, of course, is that all this was based on misinformation. They had used wrong assumptions about an unpiloted airplane, and their deficient wreckage examination gave them an incorrect flap position. Nevertheless, their "findings" provided good cover for the ongoing investigation and search efforts.

Having been in this business for so many years, I find it difficult to believe that some members of the investigation team were not aware of the shortcomings in the evidence being presented by the official investigation.

If some investigators were aware, and if they made their concerns known to the official investigation, their concerns were dismissed or ignored. When you are part of an investigation team, you are expected to express your opinions only within the investigation. You are to argue your positions privately, and never publicly.

As a team member, you agree that only one voice speaks publicly, and that voice belongs to the official investigation. It seems like everyone on the MH370 team has so far lived up to this commitment. Perhaps this book will encourage some members of the team to come forward and reveal what was happening in the background.

In this case, and at this stage where the official investigation has basically run its course, I believe that investigators who were part of the official investigation should abandon the normal protocols for information release. I believe it would be a service to aviation safety if they chose to speak up.

I will say again that I have great respect for the work done by the DST group, and by others who assisted them. Their expertise is obvious, and they did exceptional work to determine a basic track line for MH370. Their dedication is to be commended. That does not take away from their contribution, perhaps through no fault of their own, to the incorrect conclusions reached by the official investigation.

The Resumed Search for Wreckage In Early 2018

In January 2018, a privately owned company launched a second search for the wreckage of MH370. During that search, the government of Malaysia issued what they called *Operational Search Updates*. The following is a quote from the background information included with these updates, "On 10 January 2018, the Government of Malaysia entered an Agreement for the search of MH370 with Ocean Infinity Limited".

The agreement stipulated that Ocean Infinity Limited would undertake a search operation to locate MH370 within a priority search area of 25,000 square kilometers in the southern Indian Ocean. The agreement was based on the principle of "no cure, no fee", and was to be completed within a timeframe of 90 search days.

The agreement identified three distinct search areas within the 25,000 square kilometer search area, the first being a primary search area of 5,000 square kilometers, the second being 10,000 square kilometers of secondary search area, and the third being another 10,000 square kilometers of tertiary search area.

There was also a fourth search area defined in the agreement, that being a supplementary search area beyond the 25,000 square kilometers. The amount of payment for finding the wreckage, or the flight data recorders, was to increase as follows: 20 million USD if found in the primary search area, 30 million if found in the secondary search area, 50 million if found in the tertiary search area, and 70 million if found outside the 25,000 square kilometer area.

Australia committed its continued support for the new search effort by supplying technical support to the Malaysian Government. Accordingly, Australia supplied all the data related to the original search that had been suspended in January 2017.

Other support supplied by Australia included detailed analysis work on potential wreckage locations completed by the Commonwealth Scientific and Industrial Research Organisation (CSIRO). Their work on this project was commissioned by, and funded by, the ATSB. CSIRO's primary contribution was to help estimate the location of the accident site. They did this by using sophisticated drift modelling, and ocean drift experimentation using replicated wreckage pieces.

It is interesting to note that a major factor influencing the results obtained by CSIRO was that their drift modelling and research started with the assumption of there being a significant amount of floating debris, and a large ocean-bottom debris field, each caused by the breakup of the airplane after a high-speed diving crash. We know that this assumption was not accurate. We know that the airplane remained basically intact, and sank to the bottom largely intact.

The specific 25,000 square kilometer area for the new search was originally identified at a meeting, called *First Principles Review*, held in Canberra, Australia from 2 to 4 November 2016, less than three months prior to when the official search would be halted. The stated purpose of the meeting was to reassess and validate existing evidence, and to identify any new analysis that may assist in identifying the location of the missing aircraft.

The ATSB's report on that meeting (dated 20 December 2016) stated, "there were representatives at the meeting from all of the organisations participating in the Search Strategy Working Group including Australia's Defence Science and Technology Group (DST Group), Boeing, Thales, Inmarsat, the National Transportation Safety Board of the US, the Air Accidents Investigation Branch of the UK and the Department of Civil Aviation, Malaysia. In addition, there were representatives from the Commonwealth Scientific and Industrial Research Organisation (CSIRO), Geoscience Australia, Curtin University, Malaysia Airlines and the People's Republic of China".

The meeting was held with the knowledge that their ongoing search for the wreckage in the southern Indian Ocean was winding down. It was increasingly apparent that the wreckage would not be found. They were confident in their search methods, so they were able to conclude that the wreckage was not within their identified 120,000 square kilometer search zone. They used that knowledge, along with updated information from other sources, to define the most probable unsearched area where the wreckage might be located, which was the 25,000 square kilometer area used for the Malaysian Government's agreement with Ocean Infinity Limited.

In their deliberations at this *First Principles Review*, the participants continued to rely on the inaccurate conclusions about how MH370 flew to the southern Indian Ocean. Their deliberations and calculations continued to be tainted by the misguided assumptions that the airplane was unpiloted, and that the engines failed, and that MH370 had experienced a high-speed diving crash.

The ATSB's report on the *First Principles Review* confirms that their rationale for choosing the new 25,000 square kilometer search area relied on the following: 1) the assumption of an unpiloted airplane – that assumption was built into the study of the satellite communications metadata that was used to determine the potential flight path; 2) the results of the simulator work, where they assessed the parameters of an impact zone based on how far the airplane could travel in an out-of-control high-speed dive, following a double engine failure; and 3) their (inaccurate) analysis of the recovered wreckage, where they found that the flaps were retracted, and that the airplane had crashed in a high-speed dive.

By starting with these basic inaccurate assumptions, it is not surprising that the chosen 25,000 square kilometer zone of ocean bottom did not contain the wreckage of MH370. This new search had no greater chance of success than did the original search.

Similar to what had happened during the original search, some of the contributors who had an influence on choosing the new search location created very high expectations for success. In their public statements, they indicated they were able to determine the location of the wreckage with high precision.

As discussed earlier, it is never appropriate for people connected to this type of activity to create such high expectations by predicting a positive and speedy outcome. There should never be a promise of results, only a promise of effort.

7
ADDRESSING POTENTIAL PILOT MOTIVATION

The official investigation looked into the backgrounds of the pilots, and apparently found nothing problematic. But there had to have been something amiss, given that MH370 disappeared because of the actions of a pilot. Now that we are certain about what happened to MH370, the question of why it happened (what motivated the pilot) can be looked at in a realistic context.

I am not sufficiently educated in the fields of human behaviour to claim any expertise in answering the why question. Only appropriately trained professionals have credibility in assessing the pilot's motivations. Having said that, and based on the information in this book, I feel compelled to contribute some facts and thoughts on the issue of motivation. I include them here in the hope that they might assist the professionals who choose to keep looking for an answer to why. Regarding pilot motivation, these are my thoughts.

In this MH370 event, there was a high degree of pre-planning. This tells us that the two pilots were not acting together. The available evidence cannot prove this with certainty, but I think most people would agree that these were the actions of one pilot, acting alone. There are many ways for one pilot to eliminate inputs by the other pilot – each way would involve a criminal act.

I believe that the evidence points more towards the captain as the perpetrator than towards the co-pilot. You will have noticed that I have used "the pilot", or "a pilot", or "he/his" when referring to the actions of the individual who took MH370 to the southern Indian Ocean. I did this deliberately, because the available evidence cannot confirm with certainty which of the two pilots took the actions. I believe that others, with more specific information about the two pilots, will be able to make a more educated determination about which pilot was the perpetrator.

Before the flight, the airplane was uploaded with the fuel load needed to take it to the chosen ditching location. It is the captain (not the company, or a dispatcher) who always makes the final decision about how much fuel to carry for any given flight. I believe that the pilot who decided on the fuel load (the captain) is more likely to be the one who took the actions.

117

The selection of the controlled ditching site informs us about the pilot's intention. It was not some random place where the airplane was about to run out of fuel. I believe the ditching location was specifically chosen because it met a number of requirements for the pilot.

The chosen location provided the daylight conditions necessary for a successful controlled ditching. The remote location provided an ideal place to descend to the ocean surface (in the daylight) without much potential of being spotted by a passing vessel. Certainly, the remote location was an ideal place to hide the wreckage. The pilot probably researched the topography of the ocean bottom to find a location with underwater ridges and canyons that would hide the airplane, and where (even in the long term) exploration would be unlikely.

The evidence of a controlled ditching confirms the pilot's intention to make the airplane disappear. The evidence shows the intention was to keep the airplane structure intact, so the airplane would sink without releasing any floating debris. The plan was to sink the airplane with everything still inside, so as not to leave a trace.

The intent to make the airplane disappear forever puts context to other actions taken by the pilot. He made the airplane disappear from ATC right at the boundary between two control sectors, which was the location that offered the best chance of avoiding immediate attention from ATC. He chose a specific and pre-planned diversion route that gave him the best chance of avoiding active scrutiny by any military surveillance.

All the evidence tells us that this event did not happen impulsively. Everything was meticulously planned, step-by-step, and over a significant timeframe. Every action was mentally well rehearsed. There can be little doubt that the pilot checked out different aspects of his overall plan during other flights, knowing what he was eventually going to do. The evidence suggests that before the pilot attempted it for real, he was convinced it would happen seamlessly, without a chance of failure.

Even though this event was meticulously planned, it was not overly complicated. Leaving aside the elimination of the other pilot, this plan was not difficult to carry out. From an airplane operating perspective, there was nothing about this plan that required anything beyond the everyday knowledge of a trained B777 pilot.

Those who choose to study what might have motivated the pilot should consider why he specifically chose this particular flight. Malaysia Airlines has many routes that overfly vast distances of ocean, and the pilot could have chosen any one of those other flights instead of MH370.

The exact same plan (for taking over the airplane) would have worked equally well on another flight. In fact, the pilot could have avoided some of the complicating factors of MH370 by choosing a different flight. He had the option to commandeer an airplane when it was already flying in an isolated location, well outside of radar coverage. If he had commandeered an airplane when it was already in a remote location, it would have taken him significantly less time to accomplish his same goals. It would be far less complicated to make it disappear, and it would take far less time to fly it to where he could hide it forever.

The evidence informs us that MH370 flew for some six hours in a probable straight line (southbound). The airplane was capable of flying on autopilot for that entire time, without any need for a pilot to be in the cockpit. By using MH370 to implement his plan, the pilot had an extended time with unobstructed access throughout the airplane. Those who research potential motivations should consider whether having this unobstructed access could have played a role.

Remember the context – what happened is not in doubt. The pilot intentionally ended his life, and callously ended the lives of everyone else on board. He took elaborate steps to conceal his actions – forever. This was not an impulsive act. Every aspect of the flight was part of the overall plan, including the long flight south. He specifically chose MH370 when he had other alternatives. The unanswered question is, why.

My lack of training in the study of human behaviour makes me unqualified to answer the why question, which compels me to end this topic here.

8
SUMMING UP

The evidence revealed in this account of what happened clearly shows that MH370 disappeared because of the deliberate actions of a pilot. All of the evidence I used to explain what happened to MH370 was available to the official investigation, and yet they failed to uncover it.

It would be an understatement to say that the disappearance of MH370 was high profile. The fact that such a high profile investigation failed to uncover and disclose such basic evidence is cause for grave concern. What assurance can we have that future investigations will not suffer from equal ineffectiveness?

Some of the top air safety investigation agencies in the world were involved in the MH370 investigation. According to the authorities, the official accident investigation included experts from Malaysia, Australia, China, United Kingdom, United States and France.

There was also a criminal investigation side to the investigation, and it had equally impressive international representation, including by Interpol. There were other countries represented in some unofficial capacity. Many people around the world, some with claims of expertise, followed the investigation closely.

Despite the availability of all this expertise, the MH370 investigation was clearly deficient. It failed to recognize and properly interpret the evidence that was available. Lessons must be learned about what went wrong, and why it went wrong, and steps must be taken to prevent this from happening again. Once more, I am compelled to offer my thoughts.

By all accounts, the MH370 investigation was established according to international standards and agreements. When the airplane disappeared, it was the responsibility of Malaysia, the country where the airplane was registered, to take the lead. Other countries have obligations and entitlements to participate (such as the country where the airplane was manufactured, and where the engines were manufactured, etc.).

By international agreement, Malaysia was required to launch two parallel investigations. They must launch an independent safety investigation that looks for accident causation from a safety of flight perspective. They must also launch a separate criminal investigation, to look for criminal involvement. This parallel investigation setup is basically the same in every country. It is a necessary setup, and the proper setup, and I have no issue with it.

I have personally been involved in many investigations where the criminal side of the investigation maintained the lead role until a criminal act could be ruled out. In an airplane crash, it is normally easy to rule out any criminal intent. This usually happens quickly, and leadership of the investigation is turned over to the safety investigation.

It was a mistake when the Malaysian authorities failed to keep the investigation under the control of the criminal investigation. From the very beginning, there was at least the possibility of a criminal act. The safety investigation could have continued in parallel.

Airplane crashes can be problematic for criminal investigators, because they have no specific training or expertise to collect evidence in the aviation sphere. A criminal investigation is also constrained by the fact that evidence collected by safety investigators cannot be used in a criminal prosecution. To make up for their aviation-related expertise gap, the criminal investigation must hire outside experts to help them collect and interpret evidence.

What was lost when the investigation focus was shifted to a safety investigation was the opportunity for such outside experts to look at the evidence from a criminal perspective. Criminal investigators would instruct their experts to look at the recovered wreckage specifically for evidence of criminal actions. If they did their work competently, these outside experts would have reached different conclusions than those reached by the safety investigators.

When the investigation was turned over to the safety investigators, it seems the focus on looking for criminal involvement was lost. By the time the flaperon was found, the safety investigation had already declared that MH370 was an unpiloted airplane that ran out of fuel. It appears they examined the flaperon, and the section of the flap, with that evidence (bias) in mind.

It will be debated whether intentional deception could have played a part in why the evidence on the recovered wreckage pieces was not discovered and disclosed. When the ATSB released their update (in November 2016), which included their opinion that the flaps were retracted (up) at impact, I was shocked. How could they have missed such obvious evidence that actually pointed to the contrary?

It certainly looked like there was more to the story. Their conclusion at that time was a convenient fit with their rationale for continuing to search in the area where their calculations told them the wreckage would be. It provided justification for all the money spent, and for the further commitment of resources. It served the purposes of those who were dismissing the possibility of pilot involvement.

As I stated earlier, I find it difficult to believe that with all the expertise available to the MH370 investigation, nobody put the evidence together and presented it to those in charge. If that evidence was actually discovered and brought forward, and then suppressed, that would be intentional deception. If nobody discovered the evidence, that was incompetence. I believe it was incompetence.

Although MH370 was not an accident, all the elements of a typical accident investigation were employed. The primary purpose of an accident investigation is to discover safety deficiencies. The one overwhelming safety deficiency highlighted by the MH370 event is the inability of those involved to find and interpret obvious evidence.

In my work as an investigation consultant, I have opportunities to examine the work of numerous official investigation agencies, including the most highly regarded. I can assure you that the shortcomings in the MH370 investigation are not isolated to that event.

I do not mean to imply that all investigations miss the mark. Some excellent work is being done, and deficiencies are being uncovered, and safety actions are being taken. However, opportunities for safety improvements are being lost because investigators miss or misinterpret evidence.

I believe that an important safety deficiency is apparent. It is a deficiency in the accident investigation capabilities of those who took part in the MH370 investigation, and of investigation agencies generally.

I believe the identification of this deficiency provides an opportunity to assess the readiness of all investigation agencies. Every agency should be able to find and analyze the types of evidence presented in this book. This investigation work should not be beyond the capabilities of any agency that has an investigation mandate. What has been presented here is nothing more than basic accident investigation.

I address the following comments to government officials who have a responsibility to maintain an effective accident investigation response capability. They should make sure that the skills within their agency allow for the type of investigation analysis contained in this book. If the state of readiness was where it should be in accident investigation, every air safety investigator should not only be able to read and understand this book, they should be able to write it. As the MH370 investigation shows, you cannot just assume that the skills are there, even if your agency is recognized as world class.

I address the following comments to decision makers from the companies who are obliged to send experts to assist in an investigation. For MH370, these companies included Malaysia Airlines, Boeing, Rolls-Royce, etc. It is essential that the investigators sent from these companies have the necessary skills to identify and analyze basic evidence. The appropriate decision makers must take steps to ensure those skills are in place.

This book is directed at a wide audience, but allow me to address this short bit specifically to those who work as investigators, or who plan to work as investigators. The single greatest attribute for any investigator is curiosity. A burning curiosity should have motivated the MH370 investigators to not be satisfied until they had a complete understanding of every witness mark. They should have obsessed over all the possibilities for how each wreckage piece was created, and figured out how they all combined to tell a story. Curiosity alone should motivate every investigator to read this account of what happened. If you are an investigator, or plan to be one, and you are not curious enough to read this book and learn from it, then you are probably not a good fit for the profession.

All investigators need to be exposed to the investigation basics. Not everyone needs to be a specialist in every aspect of an investigation, but everyone should be able to understand the basics, and be able to contribute (at the very least, to be able to contribute curiosity). It takes a team of investigators with different skills to conduct a successful investigation. Everyone on the team can contribute to ensuring that all the appropriate questions are asked, and to ensuring that no answer is left unchallenged if any doubt about its accuracy remains.

To be effective, you do not need to be the loudest voice in the room. In fact, you should be wary of the loudest voices. Do not assume that those with the most forceful opinions are delivering the most accurate assessments. Seek out and work with those who have the expertise you need to satisfy your curiosity. Then check, and then double check.

An overactive ego can hurt your ability to find and assess evidence. I have seen this many times, even in myself. As the investigation progresses, it is hard to resist taking your best guess about what happened. You can then fall victim to looking only for evidence to prove yourself right, or to assessing evidence with a bias. You are more likely to do that if you have revealed your best guess to someone else within the team. I believe there were elements of this in the MH370 investigation.

If you have read all the way through to this point, I expect you agree with the evidence that shows an MH370 pilot intentionally ditched the airplane. This evidence is solid, but that does not mean that it will not be challenged. There are some fervent believers in the unpiloted airplane theory, or in some other theory, who will not easily be persuaded. I offer some tips on how to assess the inevitable push back that will come.

Numerous witness marks have been identified that point to an intentional controlled ditching, with the flaps extended (down). People may attempt to explain how one or more of these witness marks could have been produced in a different way than what I have explained.

Remember that any explanation that tries to counter my explanation for how an individual witness mark was made must account for all the other witness marks that are completely consistent with the one in question. Do not accept that someone has put into doubt the entire proof of a controlled ditching simply by attacking the validity of an individual witness mark. For example, if someone comes up with a different way to create the damage around the edges of the entry hole into the seal pan, ask them to explain their theory in the context of the pristine condition of the flap section, and the two directions of witness marking inside the seal pan. For their alternate theory to be valid, everything about it has to fit, the same way everything fits with the controlled ditching theory I have presented.

Each piece of evidence presented is consistent with, and is supported by, the other pieces of evidence. For example, the crushing damage on the endplate of the seal pan proves that there was a spanwise force created along the trailing edge of the right wing. The "V-shaped" black smudge witness marks show the relative positions of the flaperon and right outboard flap when that crushing damage occurred. The witness marks inside the seal pan show the movements of the recovered piece of the right outboard flap before it broke free from the wing. All of this evidence works together.

Perhaps someone will argue that the spanwise force was not created in a controlled ditching. They might suggest that a spanwise force could be created by the right wingtip striking the water while the airplane was in a steep right bank following an uncontrolled dive.

This is a good example of a theory being theoretically possible, but not applicable. It certainly is possible to create a spanwise force along the trailing edge of the right wing by striking the right wingtip into the water in a steep diving turn. However, that did not happen with MH370. There are several counter-arguments; here are two easy ones: that high-speed scenario does not account for the flaps being extended (down), or for how they got to the extended (down) position. Neither does it account for the evidence that proves the wings were level, including the trailing edge damage on the flaperon and flap section, and the twin pieces that were recovered, one from each wing.

To challenge the evidence presented here, people might come up with other theoretically possible ways to explain how some specific piece of evidence could have been created. If/when this happens, the proponents of the alternate theories should be challenged to fit their evidence into the entire stream of existing evidence. If their evidence does not fit with everything, then it can be dismissed. There is a world of difference between something being theoretically possible, and proving that it was actually a part of what happened.

As I mentioned in the introduction, I believe that when they study the evidence I have presented, the official investigation will abandon their unpiloted airplane theory. If they do not, they should be challenged. They should be asked to provide their own explanations for each of the witness marks that prove there was no unpiloted airplane. They should be reminded that at no point in their official investigation did they attempt to explain these numerous witness marks, or even to acknowledge their existence.

Tragic accidents almost always result in safety improvements, based on the safety deficiencies uncovered by the investigation. Recommendations are made, and safety barriers are put in place to make sure the same accident cannot happen again. Action can be taken to improve training, enhance procedures, and upgrade equipment and infrastructure.

MH370 was not an accident; it was a criminal act. The challenge with MH370 is to find a barrier that could prevent someone who already has direct control from carrying out an intentional act. How do you defend against a pilot who intends to destroy his or her own airplane? It is simple logic that you cannot stop someone from taking control if they already have control. This presents a significant challenge.

When an airplane is in flight, those on board are completely vulnerable to any evil-minded intent by a pilot. The inside of an airplane in flight is a unique environment; nothing else compares to it. Once the airplane is airborne, it is impossible to safely intervene from outside. The circumstances of MH370, and other rogue pilot events, show just how easy it is for a pilot, who already has complete control of the airplane, to take independent actions.

Following the crash of Germanwings Flight 9525 in 2015, several operators implemented a policy of having two people in the cockpit at all times. When a pilot leaves the cockpit, a flight attendant is called in. The thought is that this could prevent what happened on Flight 9525, where the captain left the cockpit and the co-pilot locked him out. The co-pilot then intentionally crashed the airplane.

Having a second person in the cockpit is a defense against the remaining pilot becoming incapacitated while alone, but against an intentional act it is a weak defence at best. It is not difficult to imagine how a motivated pilot could overcome that defense.

The Germanwings crash also energized ongoing studies into how to improve the psychological testing and monitoring of pilots. Hopefully, the information presented here will broaden the base of knowledge available for further research. I included my thoughts about the MH370 pilot's motivation to ensure all potential avenues of research are considered.

The disappearance of MH370 has led to an increased focus on technologies that will allow real-time tracking of airplanes, regardless of where they are flying. Tracking systems that have been limited by the effective range of radar signals are being replaced by satellite data links that live stream location data from anywhere in the world.

Like everything else in the modern world of electronics, such tracking capabilities are leapfrogging ahead as bandwidth capacities increase, and costs decrease. This problem will soon be a thing of the past.

In writing for a wide audience, I have attempted to explain the evidence using non-technical terminology. I have also provided a peek behind the curtain at how professional investigators look for, and find, and assess, evidence.

In such a short piece of writing, it is difficult to provide a full appreciation for the countless hours of tedious and detailed work necessary to review every possible explanation for each piece of evidence. In a professional investigation environment, no theory is discounted until it has been proven to not fit with the facts. In the case of MH370, a pilot-controlled ditching is the only theory that fits with every piece of evidence.

Unlike in my previous writing, this book allowed me the freedom to use the language of certainty when those words best described what the evidence shows. You can see the evidence for yourself, and the analysis of that evidence is not particularly complicated. Now that you have seen the evidence, if you hear someone say that what happened to MH370 has not been solved, you will know they have not read this book.

Because we now have a definitive answer about what happened, the question about why it happened can be assessed with the appropriate perspective. The pilot's motivation can be looked at with the knowledge that he planned for each aspect of the flight.

The pilot knew exactly what he was going to be doing during each stage of the flight, from the time of departure all the way to the controlled ditching. It is clear he knew what the consequences would be: certain death for everyone in the airplane. It is also clear that whatever forces were driving him to carry out his planned actions, they exceeded whatever capacity he had for self-restraint.

The evidence confirms that the airplane is at the bottom of the southern Indian Ocean. It is in a location specifically chosen by the pilot to make it un-findable. The fuselage of the airplane is basically intact, and all the occupants are still inside.

A valid question is, will MH370 ever be found? My answer is that it probably will be found someday, but most likely it will be a long time from now. It will rest where it is until eventually someone finds it by using a technology that has not yet been invented.

In my view, it is unrealistic to conduct any further searches. As discussed earlier, without the certainties of the unpiloted airplane theory, there are too many variables to allow realistic calculations about where to look.

The good news is that we do not need to find the airplane to solve what happened. Fortunately, the pilot's plan to make the airplane disappear was not perfect. Satellite communication technology, and drift modelling, provided the means to discover that the airplane went to the southern Indian Ocean. Fate gave us the exact wreckage pieces required to prove that the flaps were extended during a pilot-controlled ditching.

With that, we have all the evidence we need to solve the mystery of MH370. We know that this event was not caused by some defect in the airplane, or by some unknown intervention. We know that the pilot took it, and we know how he took it, and we know where he took it, and we know it was all deliberate and well planned.

There is no longer any mystery about what happened to MH370. With this book, the mystery of MH370 is solved.

ACKNOWLEDGMENTS

My investigation partners: Terry Heaslip, the best wreckage analyst in the world, and Elaine Summers, an exceptionally skilled investigator. This book could not have been written without your expertise.

Ted Parisee: thank you for creating amazing schematics and annotating photographs.

Friends and family: thank you for steering me away from excess technical jargon.

Formatting Experts team: special thanks for being an invaluable resource for publishing advice, book design and technical assistance.

LOG OF FIGURES AND PHOTO ATTRIBUTIONS

Figure	Description	Attribution
1	Boeing 777 Reference Diagram	Technical drawing by Parisee
2	Typical Wreckage Pieces from Swissair 111	From author's personal collection (the Swissair 111 Investigation Records)
3	B777 Right Wing Showing Flaperon Location	Personal photograph, annotation by Parisee
4	Recovered MH370 Flaperon	Source: Bureau d'Enquetes et d'Analyses (BEA), annotation by Parisee
5	Wreckage from Swissair 111	From author's personal collection (the Swissair 111 Investigation Records)
6	Depiction of a B777 in a High-Speed Diving Crash	Visualization by Parisee
7	Showing the Flaperon Trailing Edge Erosion Damage	Source: Direction générale de l'armement / Techniques aéronautiques (modified by ATSB), annotation by Parisee
8	A Depiction of MH370 Entering the Water in a Pilot-Controlled Ditching	Visualization by Parisee
9	The Recovered Flap Section from the Right Outboard Flap – Insert Shows Its Installed Location	Depiction by Parisee based on ATSB photograph
10	Flaperon on the Right Wing Showing Gaps at Each End	Personal photograph, annotation by Parisee
11	Inboard End of the Recovered Flap Section	Photograph by ATSB, annotation by Parisee
12	The Endplate as Viewed from Inside the Seal Pan	Photograph by ATSB, annotation by Parisee
13	Schematic of a B777 Looking from Directly Overhead	Technical drawing by Parisee
14	A View Inside the Seal Pan of the Recovered Flap Section	Photograph by ATSB, annotation by Parisee
15	Outboard End of Flaperon – Inboard End of Flap Section	Inboard end photograph by ATSB, outboard end photograph source per Figure 7 attribution, annotation by Parisee
16	The Black Smudge Marks Show that the Flaps Were Extended (Down)	Photographs by ATSB and Bill Abbott (see copyright page for details), annotation by Parisee

17	Depiction of Attachment Points – Flaps to Wing	Public domain photograph, annotation by Parisee
18	Depiction of the Support Track Architecture	Visualization by Parisee
19	Recovered Piece of the Right Outboard Flap	Photograph by ATSB, annotation by Parisee
20	Damage at the Entry Hole Into the Seal Pan	Photograph by ATSB, annotation by Parisee
21	Inside the Seal Pan – Damage from Two Different Directions	Photographs from ATSB, annotation by Parisee
22	Fractured Flap Mount – Insert Shows Fractured and Bent Push/Pull Rod	Photograph by ATSB, annotation by Parisee
23	A Close Up View of the Fractured and Bent Push/Pull Rod	Photograph by ATSB, annotation by Parisee
24	Overlapping Gouging from Compressive Buckling Loads	Photograph by ATSB, annotation by Parisee
25	Impact Witness Mark from Contact with Support Track Aft End	Photograph by ATSB, annotation by Parisee
26	Showing the Absence of Specific Damage – Proof that the Flaps Were Extended (Down)	Photographs by ATSB, annotation by Parisee
27	Depicting Two Wreckage Pieces that are Basically Twins – One from Each Side of the Airplane	Photographs sourced from documents released by *Malaysian ICAO Annex 13 Safety Investigation for MH370* – left side photographs sourced from document titled *Summary of Possible MH370 Debris Recovered* (updated 14 October 2016), item 9 – right side photographs sourced from document titled *Debris Examination Report* (updated on 30th April 2017), item 15; technical drawing and annotation by Parisee
28	The Identified Interior Wreckage Pieces from MH370	Photographs sourced from document released by *Malaysian ICAO Annex 13 Safety Investigation for MH370* titled *Summary of Possible MH370 Debris Recovered* (updated 14 October 2016), items 5, 16 and 11; annotation by Parisee
29	Depiction of the Recovered Wreckage Pieces from MH370	Source: Ministry of Transport Malaysia
30	Depiction of the Seven Handshakes	Visualization by Parisee, based on ATSB depiction in *The Operational Search for MH370* report

TECHNICAL INFORMATION SOURCES

All documentation pertaining to MH370 made available on the *Australian Transport Safety Bureau* website – atsb.gov.au/mh370

Australian Transport Safety Bureau

MH370 – Definition of Underwater Search Areas
26 June 2014 (updated 30 July 2015)

MH370 – Flight Path Analysis Update
8 October 2014

MH370 – Definition of Underwater Search Areas
3 December 2015 (updated 10 December 2015)

MH370 – Search and debris examination update
2 November 2016 (updated 18 August 2017)

MH370 – First Principles Review
2 – 4 November 2016 (published on 20 December 2016)

The Operational Search for MH370
3 October 2017

CSIRO Oceans and Atmosphere
Prepared for the Australian Transport Safety Bureau

David Griffin, Peter Oke and Emlyn Jones
The search for MH370 and ocean surface drift
Report Number: EP167888
8 December 2016

David Griffin, Peter Oke and Emlyn Jones
The search for MH370 and ocean surface drift – Part II
Report Number: EP172633
13 April 2017

David Griffin and Peter Oke
The search for MH370 and ocean surface drift: Part III, Part IV
Report Numbers: EP174155, EP177204
26 June 2017, 3 October 2017

All documentation made available on the official website for the MH370 investigation – mh370.gov.my/en

The Malaysian ICAO Annex 13 Safety Investigation Team for MH370

Factual Information – Safety Investigation For MH370
Issued on 8th March 2015 (updated on 15th April 2015)

Summary of Possible MH370 Debris Recovered
Updated 14 October 2016

Debris Examination Report – Safety Investigation For MH370
Issued on 28th February 2017 (updated on 30th April 2017)

3rd Interim Statement – Safety Investigation For MH370 (9M-MRO)
8th March 2017

Summary of Possible MH370 Debris Recovered
Updated 30 April 2017

Government of Malaysia

MH370 Operational Search Updates
Released weekly during 2018 wreckage search
All updates available at mh370.gov.my/en/mh370-underwater-search-2018

GLOSSARY OF TERMS

ACARS – ACARS is the acronym for Aircraft Communications Addressing and Reporting System. It is a digital datalink system used to send and receive messages, including automatic messages, between the airplane and ground stations.

Air Traffic Control (ATC) – ATC provides each airplane with specific guidance, such as what route to fly, and what altitude to fly at, to ensure there is a separation between all the aircraft using any given airspace.

Anomaly – First Known Anomaly – The first instance or indication of a deviation away from what is normal or expected. Investigators look for the cause of the deviation to seek out what caused it – looking for the lead event.

ATSB – Australian Transport Safety Bureau (atsb.gov.au).

Automatic Electronic Messaging – Automatic electronic messaging is accomplished through ACARS (see "ACARS").

B777 – The short form for the model of airplane involved in this occurrence, a Boeing 777-200ER.

Cruise Altitude – The cruising altitude of the airplane, as chosen by the pilots. A typical altitude for a long-range airline flight would be above 30,000 feet (9144 meters).

Depressurize – The living space in an airplane is pressurized to allow breathable air at high altitudes. The pilots can depressurize the airplane through a switch selection in the cockpit.

Distributed Hydrodynamic Forces – See "Multi-axial Load" – in the book these terms are used interchangeably.

Ditching – Pilot Controlled Ditching – A purposeful attempt to land an airplane on the surface of the water, and cause minimal damage.

Dynamic Instability – This term is used to describe an instability where oscillations continually double, and then redouble, in amplitude.

Electronic Radar Signal – See "Transponder", "Electronic Tracking" and "Radar".

Electronic Tracking – Air Traffic Control is able to track an airplane through an electronic device in the airplane called a transponder. The transponder allows ATC to see the airplane's location, altitude, direction, speed, etc.

Flail – This term is used to describe how the section of flap was thrashing around wildly after it severed from the outboard flap, and prior to it breaking free from the back of the wing.

Flaperon – A B777 has one flaperon attached to the trailing edge of each wing (see Figure 3). They are used as part of the roll control for the airplane, and are also part of the flap system where they extend and retract (travel down and up) together with the flaps.

Flap – Flaps are moveable devices mounted on the trailing edges of both wings (see Figure 1). They are extended (down) when the airplane needs more lift at lower speeds, such as during takeoff and landing. At cruise speed, they are retracted (up), and streamlined with the wing.

Flutter – Flutter is a severe and destructive vibration caused by dynamic instability. It can occur, for example, when an airplane goes beyond its normal airspeed limit.

High-speed dive – (In the context of MH370) The state of flight the airplane would have entered if it was unpiloted and had lost power on both engines at cruise altitude. The airplane would eventually enter a high-speed spiral dive where it would either break apart in the air, or crash nose first into the ocean surface.

Hypoxia – Hypoxia occurs when a body is deprived of an adequate oxygen supply.

IGARI Waypoint – This was the first electronic waypoint along the route of travel for MH370 on its way to its destination.

Lead Event – The initial event that starts the chain of events leading to the final outcome. The first known anomaly with MH370 was the disappearance of the transponder signal. The lead event would be whatever caused the transponder signal to disappear.

MH370 – Malaysia Airlines Flight 370.

Multi-axial Load – Specific to MH370, this term is used to describe how when the airplane entered the water at high speed, the non-compressible (but fluid) water exerted forces inside the fuselage that were equal in all directions, causing an explosive force acting in all directions.

Official Investigation – For the investigation of MH370, Malaysia set up a Joint Investigation Team (JIT) consisting of specialists from Malaysia, Australia, China, the UK, the US, and France.

Radar – Primary Radar – Primary Radar sends out radio waves that bounce off an object and return to the radar receiver, thus revealing where the object is located. When used with a transponder in an airplane, significantly more information is returned from the airplane – see "Transponder".

Satellite Data – In relation to MH370, satellite data refers to communications between the airplane and a satellite network operated by Inmarsat.

Search Area Coordinates – The coordinates, in latitude and longitude, of four corners of the search areas, as determined by the official investigation.

Technical Failure – Also referred to as a Technical Event, a technical failure refers to a failure in some piece of equipment, as opposed to an operational failure, which is a human failure.

Track – A reference to the line of travel of an airplane – the line that depicts where it has been during its flight, and the line that projects where it is going.

Transponder – Through a transponder working with radar, airplanes send electronic tracking information to ATC. This information allows air traffic controllers to see the airplane's location, altitude, direction, speed, etc.

Witness Mark – (In the context of MH370) A scratch, or dent, or cut, or smudge, or abrasion, or similar mark that can reveal the interaction between structural pieces that make contact with each other during an impact.

CONTENTS

Made in the USA
Coppell, TX
10 March 2020